AN INTRODUCTION TO
Trees

BY JOHN KIERAN

Illustrations by Michael H. Bevans

HANOVER HOUSE

Garden City, New York

INDEX

FOREWORD

Like its companion works, *An Introduction to Birds* and *An Introduction to Wild Flowers*, this is a book for beginners and has been made as simple as possible. It is offered as a help in learning to recognize and name the more common trees of our city streets, our suburban lawns, our village greens, and our travel-packed parkways as well as some representative trees of the fields and forests of North America. Birds, flowers, and trees call for a different approach in each case. Most of our birds are migratory. They come and go and you have to be on the alert to see them at the right time and place. Most of our wild flowers have only a brief blooming period. You must look for them at a certain time of year if you wish to find them in all their beauty and fragrance. But the trees we have always with us. With them there is no hurry. You can walk slowly and take your time in making their acquaintance. They will wait for you. They stand there Winter and Summer, year in and year out, in all kinds of weather. Many have been standing for a century or more. There are Douglas Firs standing today on the Pacific Coast where they stood when Columbus landed on San Salvador in 1492. Some of the Sequoias of the Sierras are older than Christendom. Trees are not only useful and beautiful but the oldest and largest living things on earth.

Probably everybody can recognize a few trees, at least in a general way. They may recognize them as Oaks or Maples or Pines, but there are many kinds of Oak, Maple, and Pine. Which one of the Oaks or Maples or Pines is this one at the roadside? If such a question arises in your mind, watch your next step. It may lead to a lifetime interest in trees with added knowledge and greater enjoyment year by year. There are many good field guides to our shrubs and trees and there are standard reference works in botany that contain detailed descriptions of all the trees native to North America, but the very wealth of the material and the technical terms necessarily used in such volumes may baffle the beginner. The modest aim here is to provide the novice with an elementary guide to a friendly acquaintance with some of the trees that are near at hand and under whose shade we often wander. After that, the reader whose interest is aroused may move ahead to wider and richer researches in field and forest with other and more capable guides. This book will serve its purpose best if it is not only AN INTRODUCTION TO TREES but an introduction to other books of wider scope by authors of recognized authority in the study of trees. There is no lack of such books and authors for any region of temperate North America.

This continent is fortunate in its wealth of trees and we have variety as well as abundance. There are well over a thousand different species of trees native to North America and there are many introduced species that either have been here so long or have been so widely planted that they are now accepted, like other good immigrants, as "naturalized citizens." You will find some of these introduced trees in this book because they so often meet the eye along the city street or down the country lane. A few shrubs also have been included for various reasons. One is that the dividing line between shrubs and trees often is merely a matter of form. A species that is a tree in one region may shrink to shrub size in another region. But more important than that is the fact that shrubs, like their loftier relatives, attract the notice of the walker in the fields and woods and it's natural to be curious about the names of the more common ones that are often encountered.

The knowledge of a few basic points about trees will give the beginner a start on firm ground. Trees belong to that great division of botanical life called Flowering Plants. It may come as a surprise to some readers that all healthy mature trees have flowers of some kind, the Elm as well as the Magnolia, the Oak as well as the Cherry. Not all individual trees, however, have fruit. In some species there are male and female flowers —or "staminate" and "pistillate" flowers, as the botanists prefer it—that are produced on separate trees, and in such cases only the trees with the female or pistillate flowers can bear fruit. Incidentally, "fruit" is a term that needs explaining for beginners. Whatever contains the seed of any tree is the fruit, and it may be a nut, a berry, a cone, a capsule, a bean, a "pome" such as an apple, a "drupe" of the plum type, an acorn, or any number of other things depending upon the kind of tree that produces it. There are many species of Maple but all Maples have one thing in common and that is the fruit that children call "keys" and botanists call "samaras." The acorn is the mark of the Oak group.

Aside from such simple and basic matters, the first rule to follow if you want to know the trees is: Look at them. Look closely at the bark, the leaf, the flower, the fruit and, when the leaves are off, look at the leaf scars—the "fingerprints" of lost foliage—and the buds that promise new leaves "when Spring trips north again this year." Most trees, at one season or another, have distinctive features that are easily noted even by a novice in the field. It may be the bark, the leaf, the flower, or the fruit, or a combination of such features. In the White Birch and the Beech the bark is distinctive. The mitten-shaped leaves of the Sassafras are distinctive as are the star-shaped leaves of the Sweet Gum. The flowers of the Horse Chestnut, the Buckeyes, the Magnolias, and the Tulip Trees are distinctive and so are the fruits that follow in each case. Dried fruits that cling to bare branches in Winter are helpful marks of identity in many species of tree and shrub.

Once you have recognized a tree by its distinctive features, take note of less striking details at different times of the year. You wouldn't know a man very well if you didn't recognize him when he changed his suit. You will not know a tree well until you recognize it in Winter as well as Summer. Follow the march of the seasons and watch the changes as

The faint fresh flame of the young year flushes
From leaf to flower and flower to fruit.

All of us, old and young, love to walk in the woods. Standing in a grove of great Hemlocks, it is easy to understand how some of the pagans of ancient days made trees the object of worship. They are beautiful; they are majestic; they are enduring. There is endless enjoyment in store for anyone who seeks a closer acquaintance with these ageless and admirable benefactors of mankind.

John Kieran

AMERICAN YEW; GROUND HEMLOCK

(*Taxus canadensis*)

If the way to learn a subject is from the ground up, it seems sensible to start the study of trees by becoming acquainted with the American Yew or Ground Hemlock. You probably will have to bend over to get a close look at it. Throughout most of its range—from Newfoundland to Manitoba and south to Virginia, Kentucky and Iowa—it is a mere shrub of feathery evergreen foliage slanting upward a few feet from the forest floors where it flourishes, though on occasion it may reach a height of 5 feet or more. It would take some stretch of the imagination to call it a tree, but it grows among trees, appearing most frequently and abundantly in woods where tall evergreens predominate, and there its foliage, that justifies its secondary name of Ground Hemlock, may leave a beginner puzzled as to whether he is looking at a full-grown American Yew or a little Hemlock just starting out in life.

There are detailed differences that a botanist would point out in a jiffy, but the quickest way to settle the matter is to flip the branchlet over and look at the lower side of the leaf spray. The linear leaves or needles of the American Yew are green on both sides. They are a lighter green on the lower surface, or even a yellowish-green, but you can see plainly that they are green, whereas the Hemlock needles are decidedly silvery or pale gray on the lower surface. Once you make this comparison, you never again need be baffled by the superficial resemblance of the foliage of the lowly American Yew to that of any Hemlock, large or small.

One of the attractive features of this evergreen shrub is the bright red, berry-like fruit, curiously open at the outer end, that appears late in the season amid the dark foliage of some of the plants—the pistillate or "female" ones. The European Yew, which grows to a larger size and, according to English legend furnished the bows for Robin Hood and his merry men in Sherwood Forest, produces such quantities of pollen on the staminate or "male" trees that a branch shaken by the wind—or by hand—in the blossoming season will send clouds of the light-colored pollen into the air like smoke. That's why Tennyson in the *Holy Grail* had the monk Ambrosius say to Sir Percivale:

O brother, I have seen this Yew Tree smoke,
Spring after Spring, for half a hundred years.

[9]

BALSAM FIR

(Abies balsamea)

Almost certainly this is an old friend, known and cherished since childhood, though perhaps under another name. This is by all odds the favorite "Christmas tree" in North American homes at Yuletide. That's because it has two advantages over other evergreens that are used as Christmas trees. It holds its needles for a longer period after cutting than most of its rivals for the job, and it is superlatively aromatic. We have numerous native Firs, most of them inhabitants of the cooler regions of the Pacific Northwest, and they are a fragrant group as a whole. The crushed leaves, the bruised bark, or the punctured "resin blisters" will, in most cases, give off a pleasant odor. But the Balsam, as it is called, is by far the most pleasantly odorous member of this redolent group.

At any distance Firs and Spruces will look much alike to a beginner, but there is one difference that is easily noted. The cones of all our Firs grow upright on the branchlets, whereas the cones of Spruces hang down. Another point of difference can best be cleared up with the aid of a pocket magnifying glass. Spruce needles stripped from a twig leave little projections rough to the touch along the bare twig. If Fir needles are stripped in the same fashion, the "leaf scars" that remain on the twig will be tiny circles. If you wish to pursue the matter further under the magnifying glass, you will see that Spruce needles are squarish in cross section while Fir needles are narrowly rectangular.

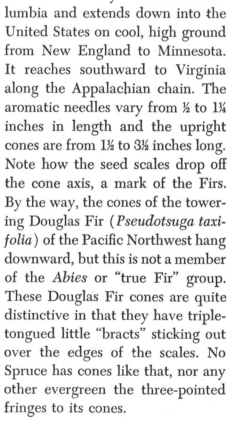

The Balsam is a tree of medium size that ranges from Labrador to Yukon Territory and British Columbia and extends down into the United States on cool, high ground from New England to Minnesota. It reaches southward to Virginia along the Appalachian chain. The aromatic needles vary from ½ to 1¼ inches in length and the upright cones are from 1½ to 3½ inches long. Note how the seed scales drop off the cone axis, a mark of the Firs. By the way, the cones of the towering Douglas Fir (*Pseudotsuga taxifolia*) of the Pacific Northwest hang downward, but this is not a member of the *Abies* or "true Fir" group. These Douglas Fir cones are quite distinctive in that they have triple-tongued little "bracts" sticking out over the edges of the scales. No Spruce has cones like that, nor any other evergreen the three-pointed fringes to its cones.

EASTERN HEMLOCK
(*Tsuga canadensis*)

This is one of the best known and also one of the easiest to identify of all the evergreens native to North America. It's like the Robin among birds or the common White Daisy among wild flowers. It is so familiar to most of us who roam the outdoors that it can be used as a standard of comparison in describing less common species or those more difficult to identify. There are other Hemlocks native to North America—the Western Hemlock and the Mountain Hemlock familiar to woodchoppers and lumber companies of the Pacific Northwest, and the Carolina Hemlock of the Allegheny ridges from southwestern Virginia to Georgia—but in ordinary conversation outside of lumber camps, lumberyards, or botanical conferences, the name "Hemlock" is usually taken as a reference to this species. In short, and without any law covering the matter, to the man in the street or the boy in the woods, this is *the* Hemlock.

There are few trees more attractive to the eye. This is a lovely, lofty evergreen of graceful pyramidal shape and feathery, dark foliage of linear leaves or needles about ½ inch long that spread out on either side of the branchlets to give a "flat" appearance to the leaf spray. Among the evergreens this is one of the distinguishing features of the Eastern Hemlock and another is the contrast between the dark green color of the upper side of a leaf spray and the pale gray or silvery sheen of the lower side. The tiny cones, rarely as much as 1 inch long, hang on the tips of the branchlets through the year and the brown cones of the previous season and the green cones of the current season often are found on the tree at the same time. The range of the Eastern Hemlock is from Nova Scotia and New Brunswick westward to Minnesota and south along the ridges to Georgia and Alabama. At maturity it may reach a height of 100 feet or so, with a trunk diameter of 4 feet or more, though such trees are exceptional. In general it is a narrowly pyramidal tree with a conical top like a church steeple. It prefers rocky hillsides and often forms imposing groves on the sides of steep ravines, but it is also found along roadsides, in dooryards, or planted for ornamental purposes on private or public ground. The cones of the other Hemlocks are larger than those of this species and the foliage not so flat in appearance. The Western Hemlock is the giant of the group and often reaches a height of 150 feet. This abundant tree of the Pacific Northwest is a fast grower and has become a real rival of the Spruces as a source of wood pulp for paper manufacturing and plastic industries.

RED SPRUCE

(Picea rubens)

As a whole, Spruces are a group of trees that are tall, dark, handsome, and almost forbidding in appearance where they extend in vast forests over the colder regions of the Northern Hemisphere. Most of the individual Spruce trees of North America are Canadian by birth and preferred residence. Where they extend down into the United States they begin to climb to enjoy cooler air, which means that they are found on the Rocky Mountain slopes of the West and the Appalachian ridges of the East. At lower levels the Spruces of this continent stick to Canada and the northern tier of the United States. There are two species, however, the colorful Blue Spruce, native to a portion of the Rocky Mountain region, and the imported Norway Spruce, that are widely planted across the country for decorative purposes, and these Spruces you may find wherever care and feeding will keep them alive.

To the beginner most Spruce trees will look much alike. Learning to distinguish one species from another will take some time and study. The immediate problem for the beginner is not how to distinguish one species of Spruce from another but how to know the Spruces from the Hemlocks and Firs. That's a fairly easy matter. In most of our North American species the Spruce needles are short, slightly curving, fairly stiff, and sharp-pointed and they grow in such fashion that the branchlets seem "armed at all points." Have you seen brushes with which the insides of bottles are cleaned? The "business end" of such a brush is a cylinder of bristles that stick out in all directions. That will give you some idea—a little exaggerated, perhaps—of how Spruce leaves are arranged along the branchlets. It's quite different from the comparatively flat or 2-ranked foliage of the Hemlocks and the upward sweep of the Fir foliage. There are other differences, such as the stubby, peg-like projections from which the Spruce leaves start and the way the cones of our Spruces hang below the horizontal while our Fir cones are carried erect on the branchlets. The Red Spruce, shown here, is an eastern species that ranges from eastern Canada south to North Carolina and Tennessee on high ground. The 4-sided needles, about ½ inch, are stiff and slightly curved, and the cones average about 1½ inches in length. The Spruces are the trees that furnish the bulk of the wood pulp used in the manufacturing of paper of all kinds, including the paper on which this is printed.

AMERICAN LARCH; TAMARACK

(Larix laricina)

The Larches or Tamaracks are an odd lot. They have linear leaves or needles and they produce cones like "the murmuring Pines and the Hemlocks," but they shed their leaves in the Autumn, which is the mark of the "deciduous" trees. Larch is the Old World name for the group, but Tamarack seems to be the choice on this side of the Atlantic. Under either name, this species is the most widespread of the group in North America and one of the hardiest trees on this continent. It ranges from Labrador to Alaska and from West Virginia on a slant across the United States to British Columbia. It likes wet ground and swamps, but it takes to the hillsides in many northerly portions of its range. It has been known to reach a height of 100 feet, but ordinarily it is a tree of medium size and at the northern limit of its range, which is approximately the "tree limit" of North America, it is little more than a ragged wind-blown shrub.

In the Winter it has a forlorn look like a dead Spruce, but the warmth of Spring brings out the clumps of 6 to 16 linear leaves, about 1 inch in length, that sprout in tufts from the tops of short spurs or "miniature stumps" along the branchlets. Unless you look closely you may miss the little staminate and pis-

tillate flowers that ultimately produce the ⅜-inch cones along the same branchlets and put the tree and all other Larches or Tamaracks among the "Conifers" or cone bearers in the botanical world. In the early stages the developing pistillate flowers are attractive pink or reddish outgrowths along the tan branchlets, a feature that gave the tree the name of "Epinette Rouge" or "Red Spinelet" among French Canadians. The European Larch (*Larix decidua*), frequently planted for ornament in this country, has that same feature and among those who took note of it was Alfred Tennyson when he began one quatrain of *In Memoriam* with the line:

When rosy plumelets tuft the larch ...

In the Pacific Northwest you will find the Western Larch (*Larix occidentalis*), the big brother of the American Larch and an important tree in the lumber industry. Its cones are about twice the size of those of the American Larch.

EASTERN WHITE PINE

(*Pinus strobus*)

The Pines are a widespread group of useful and, for the most part, graceful evergreens that range from coast to coast in North America and from the Gulf of Mexico to the Arctic wasteland. Many of our Pines have long, flexible, and odorous linear leaves or needles, but there is an easy way to distinguish even those that have comparatively short or stiff needles from any Yew, Fir, Hemlock, or Spruce. There are more than twenty species of Pine in North America but, with the exception of the Single-leaved Pine of narrow range in the Southwest, the linear leaves of all our Pines come in clusters or bundles ("fascicles" to the botanist) of from 2 to 5 needles each. The number of needles in a bundle, the varying lengths of the needles, and the shapes, sizes, and details of the cones, usually make it fairly easy to distinguish one species of Pine from another.

The needles of the Eastern White Pine and the Western White Pine come in bundles of fives, for instance, and so do the needles of the tallest of our Pines, the Sugar Pine of Oregon and California. But the range of the Eastern White Pine is from Newfoundland to Manitoba and south to Georgia and Iowa and over that area it is the only Pine to display needles 5 to a bundle. Where the Western White Pine and the Sugar Pine meet in Oregon and California, the enormous stout cones—up to 18 inches! —of the Sugar Pine are distinctive. The flexible, lustrous, and pleasantly aromatic needles of the valuable and beautiful Eastern White Pine are from 3 to 5 inches long and the drooping cones, looking somewhat like moldy cigars as they mature, may be from 4 to 10 inches in length. The early settlers and pioneers found great areas covered with pure stands of Eastern White Pine in the northern woods. Those trees are gone. They were used to build our civilization.

PITCH PINE
(*Pinus rigida*)

Though it may reach a height of 75 feet, the Pitch Pine more often is a much smaller, chunky tree holding stubbornly to wind-swept ground where few other trees could survive. It is found on offshore islands, sandy wastes, barren ground, and rocky ledges from Maine to Ontario and southward to western Georgia and the hills of Tennessee and Kentucky. Its rigid and usually

curving needles, 3 to 5 inches long, come 3 to a bundle and its squat cones, 1 to 3 inches long and almost as broad as they are long, are armed with sharp prickles. After they shed their seeds, the empty cones, frequently found in clusters, may cling to the trees for years. A sticky pitch oozes out of buds and branches at the least provocation, or even with no provocation at all. Hence the name Pitch Pine.

LONGLEAF PINE
(*Pinus australis*)

Here is another Pine whose needles come 3 to a bundle and whose cones are furnished with sharp prickles, but there is little danger of mistaking this tree for any of its relatives. The shining needles that give it the name of Longleaf Pine

are from 8 to 20 inches in length and as flexible as they are lustrous. On the old trees, which may reach a height of 120 feet, the foliage looks like graceful green drapery, but in the saplings the effect is even more artistic because at eye level each cluster of the extraordinary foliage seems to rise and fall away like a little green fountain. The stout cones are from 6 to 10 inches long and the orange-brown bark of the older trees is set off in irregular rectangles in a way to give the trunk something of a tiled appearance. The Longleaf Pine is found on the Atlantic Coastal Plain from Virginia to Florida and in the lowlands of the Gulf States, where it is as decorative as it is useful for timber and turpentine. There are other Pines of North America whose needles come 3 to a bundle, but always there are differences in leaf, cone, bark, or other detail by which you may know them.

RED PINE; NORWAY PINE
(*Pinus resinosa*)

The Red or Norway Pine and the Yellow or Shortleaf Pine are two tall trees of the eastern half of North America that usually produce their needles in bundles of twos, but there is no difficulty in distinguishing one from the other. The Red Pine is the northerly species and is found in dry woods from Newfoundland to Manitoba and south to West Virginia, Michigan, Wisconsin, and Minnesota. The Yellow Pine is the southerly species and occurs in dry, sandy soil from New York westward to Missouri and south to the Gulf Coast area. Where the ranges overlap, the Red Pine may be known by the fact that its 2-inch blunt cones are "unarmed" whereas the cones of the Yellow Pine, though similar in size and shape, have small but decided prickles. The Yellow Pine needles may be from 3 to 5 inches long but the Red Pine needles average about 5 inches long and may reach 6 inches or more in length. A considerable difference in the bark of the trunk, more easily seen than described, will soon become apparent to those who look closely at trees.

PINYON PINE
(*Pinus edulis*)

The scientific name of this little tree means "edible Pine." Not the whole tree, of course; just the pleasant-tasting seeds discarded by the broad, lumpy little cones about 2 inches in length no matter in what direction you measure them. The Pinyon Pine is native to the high ground—5000 to 10,000 feet altitude—of Arizona, New Mexico, Utah, and Colorado, but for the edible seeds that are marketed as "Pinyon nuts" or "Indian nuts"

and also for ornamental purposes, it has been widely cultivated and is found in many sections of the United States. The needles average a trifle over 1 inch in length, are rather stiff, and usually come in bundles of twos, though bundles of threes also are found. There is a Single-leaf Pinyon of somewhat more westerly range and lower ground that reaches into southern California and also produces an edible seed for market. The feature of this tree, as its name implies, is that its needles, 1 to 2 inches in length, occur separately and not in bundles, which makes it unique among all our North American Pines.

[16]

BALD CYPRESS
(*Taxodium distichum*)

Put on boots or take to a boat if you wish to become acquainted with the Bald Cypress in its native haunts. There is no difficulty in recognizing the tree. The difficulty is in approaching it. Here and there you may find a few of these trees on fairly solid ground but, for the most part, the Bald Cypress is a towering tree of the southern swamps and usually is found with its flaring or buttressed trunk rising out of mud or shallow water and reaching skyward to a height of 80 or 100 feet, or even 150 feet in exceptional cases. It ranges from southern New Jersey to Florida on the Atlantic Coastal Plain, across the Gulf Coast lowlands to Texas and Mexico, and up the Mississippi Basin as far as Illinois and Indiana.

The sharp-pointed objects shown rising out of the water around the base of the tree in the illustration are called "knees" and are curious projections growing out of the widespread roots of the tree. Some persons hold to the opinion that their function is to help anchor the tree in soft ground and others say that their purpose is to provide an added supply of air for roots that are continually under water. Whatever the explanation of their existence, they are an added feature in a tree that is odd in more ways than one. Pushing through a swamp in a boat, you might recognize the Bald Cypress by the buttressed base of the trunk alone. It has needles for foliage and it produces cones, but it is not an evergreen. Like the Tamarack or Larch, it is an exception among our cone bearers to that extent. Its needles, somewhat similar in appearance to those of the Hemlock and green or greenish-yellow on both sides like those of the Yew, fall in the Autumn like the foliage of the Ash, or Maple. The cones are shaped as shown in the illustration and rarely more than 1 inch in diameter. But these are needless details. The Bald Cypress is a majestic tree that has no rival of similar appearance in its water-logged realm. You will know it on sight and gaze upon it with due respect. The wood is light but durable when exposed to the weather and is much used for casks, shingles, and railroad ties.

ARBOR VITAE;
NORTHERN WHITE CEDAR
(*Thuja occidentalis*)

It isn't easy for a beginner to learn to distinguish the Arbor Vitae or Northern White Cedar from the Coast, Atlantic, or Southern White Cedar at a glance. There are other Cedars and Cypresses and allied Junipers across the country to add to the difficulty, but go slowly and cautiously among these evergreens of curious foliage and soon you will sort out the common species of your region. The Arbor Vitae in the wild is a narrowly pyramidal tree up to 50 or 60 feet in height with flat sprays of heavy foliage consisting of tiny leaves tightly braided along the branchlets. It is most easily recognized by the fruit, as shown, a narrow, upright cone ½ inch or so in length, opening at the outer end when ripe. This is a northerly tree found in wet ground from Quebec to Saskatchewan and extending down into the United States, climbing higher as it goes southward. It is common in cultivation as a trimmed hedge tree.

COAST or SOUTHERN WHITE CEDAR
(*Chamaecyparis thyoides*)

The foliage of this small to medium-size evergreen much resembles that of the Arbor Vitae or Northern White Cedar but the cones are quite different in character. All of the *Thuja* group have the little cylindrical cones that open from the outer end toward the base and all of the *Chamaecyparis* clan, including the great Port Orford Cedar (*Chamaecyparis lawsoniana*) of the Pacific Coast, have little globular cones that split toward the center in releasing the seed. As the various common names of this species imply, it is found in swamps and wet ground generally from southern Maine down the Atlantic Coastal Plain to Florida and across the Gulf States into Mississippi. That leaves little ground for confusion with the more northerly Arbor Vitae and, in the comparatively narrow region where their ranges overlap, the difference in the cones will easily distinguish one species from the other. The globular cones of the Coast, Atlantic, or Southern White Cedar are about ⅓ inch in diameter.

COMMON JUNIPER

(Juniperus communis)

There are Junipers of one kind or another from coast to coast over most of North America and they vary in size and shape from creeping shrubs to upstanding trees of picturesque appeal. They are evergreens and some of them display foliage rather similar in general appearance to that of the *Thuja* group or the *Chamaecyparis* clan mentioned on the opposite page, but you will recognize the Junipers easily because they are our only evergreens whose fruits are "berries" to the eye even if they are "cones with fleshy coverings" to the botanist. The stringy bark, the inner wood, the foliage, and the berry-like fruit of the Junipers are aromatic, much more so in some species than in others. The species shown here is a hardy shrub or small tree of rocky slopes, old pastures, and poor ground generally from Labrador to Alaska across Canada and all over the United States except the extreme Southwest and Southeast. The ½-inch needles are very sharp and, unlike most leaves, are gray above and green underneath. The pea-sized aromatic blue berry has a whitish bloom.

RED CEDAR

(Juniperus virginiana)

Springing up at random in poor soil or rocky ground from Maine to Florida and westward across the United States to the foothills of the Rockies, Red Cedars somehow give the impression of having been planted there by loving hands and carefully trimmed for decorative purposes. They are lovely and useful aromatic trees. They furnish the wood for "cedar closets" and "cedar chests," though they are not Cedars but Junipers as you may know by the pea-sized blue-gray berries that are their fruit. Most Junipers have male flowers on one tree and female flowers on another and only the trees with female or pistillate flowers bear fruit. Once you become acquainted with the group by means of the fruit, you soon will recognize Junipers, with or without fruit. Red Cedars at maturity are green spires 30 to 50 feet tall, or even taller in some cases. On young shoots they have the sharp-pointed foliage of the Common Juniper but on older branches they have braided foliage of tiny leaves somewhat like that of the *Thuja* or *Chamaecyparis* group.

[19]

REDWOOD
(*Sequoia sempervirens*)

The only rival of the Redwood on the face of the earth is its close relative and near neighbor of the Sierras, the Big Tree or *Sequoia gigantea*. These towering trees need no long technical description. To see them is to recognize them and to walk among them is an inspiring and almost overpowering experience. The great groves are meccas for thousands of tourists every year. In such places the massive trunks, reaching upward like great pillars to vanish somewhere in the dark canopy of evergreen foliage far overhead, lend an air of majesty—almost a touch of eternity—to the scene.

The Redwood is the tallest tree in the world, some of them reaching well over 300 feet in height. The Big Tree is bulkier of bole, greater in total tonnage, and of much longer life. It is believed that the Big Tree may reach an age of 4000 to 5000 years, but the longest life span of record for the Redwood is about 1400 years. The Redwood is much more abundant and is found along a 500-mile strip of the Pacific coastal area extending from southern Oregon to Monterey in California. The strip is roughly 30 miles wide, which means that it stretches from the ocean front inland to an altitude of 3000 feet on the slope of the coastal range of the Rockies. The Big Trees, so few and so much treasured that every grove is charted and named and each tree is counted and numbered, are restricted to a small section of the western slope of the Sierra Nevadas in central California from an altitude of 4300 to 8500 feet. The Redwoods are fed with moisture from the fogs that roll in from the Pacific Ocean. The Big Trees are watered by the eternal snows of the Sierras. The Redwood cones, shown here, are about 1 inch in diameter and the oval cones of the Big Tree are 2 or 3 inches long. That the tiny seeds in these cones produce such trees is almost incredible!

GINKGO; MAIDENHAIR TREE

(*Ginkgo biloba*)

This tree, imported from China, is found in rows along the streets and in the parks of many cities in the United States. It is easily recognized by the curious shape of its leaves and, when the leaves are off, by the short twigs that look like miniature stumps along the bare branches. There are male and female trees and the male is preferred for planting be-

cause the yellowish plum-like fruits that are produced in abundance by mature female trees litter the ground or the sidewalks beneath them. The crushed fruit has a bad odor and a worse taste but the kernel of the ½-inch round stone inside is sold for food in China and Japan. Fossil prints of Ginkgo leaves have been found, indicating that it must have existed millions of years ago just about as it does today. The name Maidenhair Tree is a reference to the shape of the leaves, somewhat like Maidenhair Fern divisions.

BLACK WILLOW

(*Silex nigra*)

Without any question, a beginner will be lost among the more than 100 species of Willow that as mere shrubs or trees up to 100 feet in height are found in various sections of North America. The best that the novice can do is to learn to know a Willow from any other tree, scrape an acquaintance with a few species, and leave the others to later study with a field guide or botanical textbook. As a rule, all Willows bear either male or female catkins and the female or pistillate catkins produce tiny and narrowly pear-shaped pods containing seeds with silky down attached. Willows are commonly found in moist ground and along water courses and long, narrow leaves are a badge of the tribe. The Black Willow, pictured here, may be found as a shrub or a tree up to 60 feet more in height from New Brunswick and Quebec across the continent to the foothills of the Rockies and southward as far as North Carolina, Tennessee, Alabama, and Arkansas. The leaves are 2 to 6 inches long and the expanded Spring catkins from 1 to 3 inches in length. On the lower twig, shown here, note the tiny fringes at the base of the leaves. These are the "stipules" found on many Willows, especially on shoots.

[21]

PUSSY WILLOW
(*Salix discolor*)

About the only time the ordinary passerby recognizes a Pussy Willow is in the early Spring when the famous catkins are on display, though it is more or less common as a shrub or small tree in moist ground or along ponds, streams, and lakes from Labrador to Alberta and south to Virginia, Kentucky, and Missouri. It is also much planted for ornament and the bare branchlets are sold by florists in late Winter to purchasers who put them in water at home and watch the flower buds burst open and the glorious catkins come into full bloom. Here is a chance to put a magnifying glass to good use by looking through it at the pollen-laden staminate catkins at the peak of production. You can do this conveniently at home, but you may have to compete with the early bees that are working on the flowers if you try it outdoors. The leaves that come later are from 1½ to 4 inches long, bright green above, whitish on the underside, and quite variable in shape, but on the average much broader than the typical long, narrow leaf that marks the Willow clan from a distance.

WEEPING WILLOW
(*Salix babylonica*)

This is a tree that has spread from its native China to temperate regions all over the world because of its ornamental value. It was introduced into Europe from Asia and from Europe to North America where it may be found almost anywhere in moist ground from Quebec to British Columbia and southward to the Gulf of Mexico. Its greenish-yellow catkins are not at all spectacular. In fact, most persons at any distance probably mistake them for early foliage. The striking feature of the Weeping Willow, of course, is the extraordinary length of the thin, pendulous branchlets clothed with typical narrow Willow leaves 4 to 5 inches in length. The trees may reach a height of 70 feet, with a full, round crown carried by a stout trunk as much as 6 feet in diameter. By a lake, or hanging over a stream, the effect is decidedly attractive to the eye. One reason for the abundance of the Weeping Willow is that it is easily propagated by slips and a fast grower when it takes root.

EASTERN COTTONWOOD

(Populus deltoides)

This is one of the most widespread trees in temperate North America and may be found, mostly in lowlands and along water courses, from the Atlantic Coast to the foothills of the Rockies and from southern Canada to the Gulf of Mexico. It is one of the many Poplars native to this continent and has the faults and virtues of others of the clan. It springs up readily and is a fast grower but, like most fast growers, it is not a strong tree and often suffers breakage from storms. The Cottonwood may attain 100 feet in height and its network of fine, fibrous rootlets that reach out a long way for moisture enables it to flourish where many other trees could not survive. For this reason it is often a valuable shade tree where shade is at a premium.

The Poplars are close relatives of the Willows, as is indicated by the much similar way in which they display their flowers and produce their winged seeds. The Poplar flowers, like those of the Willows, are arranged in catkins that appear before the leaves are out, and the staminate and pistillate catkins are on different trees. The pistillate or female catkins produce strings of seed capsules that eventually turn loose tiny seeds with fine,

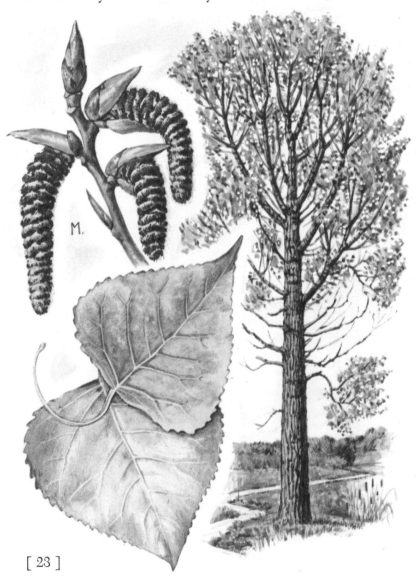

white, cottony, thread-like attachments that aid their distribution by the wind. But where the Willows as a group are noted for long, narrow leaves on very short stalks, the Poplars have broad leaf blades held well away from the branchlets by long "petioles." In most species of Poplar there is a curious flattening of the petiole that produces a shimmering effect in the foliage. This is explained in detail in the description of the Quaking Aspen on the next page.

Among the Poplars you will recognize the Cottonwood by its triangular leaves, 3 to 7 inches long, petiole included, with the blades sharp-pointed and toothed, as shown. Other distinctive features are yellowish twigs and conical Winter buds about ½ inch long and quite gummy. The male catkins, 3 to 5 inches long, are fuller and rounder than the pistillate catkins that eventually lengthen to the cottony "necklace" stage that accounts for the name, Necklace Poplar, sometimes applied to this species. The catkins usually are so numerous that they litter the ground.

QUAKING ASPEN; TREMBLING ASP
(*Populus tremuloides*)

Whether it is called Quaking Aspen or Trembling Asp, the name comes from the way the shining leaves quiver in the slightest breeze. This is due to a gradual flattening of the leaf stalk or "petiole" in a vertical plane from the branchlet to the base of the leaf blade. Thus the leaf blade is not only lightly held in place, but the flattened surface of the petiole, at right angles to the plane of the leaf blade, offers another purchase for any breeze that may be stirring. The long-petioled leaves are 1½ to 3 inches in diameter, almost round in outline though the tip is pointed, and rather shiny above and below. This member of the Poplar group spans the continent but is rather a northerly species and is not found in the Gulf States. It springs up quickly on burnt ground and in its younger years has a bark greenish-white or cream in color. Popple is still another name for this tree.

LARGE-TOOTHED ASPEN
(*Populus grandidentata*)

Though this member of the Poplar clan is well named and may be distinguished by the large teeth of the leaves that measure 2½ to 4 inches in length, it is more easily recognized by the white, cottony covering of the lower surface of the leaves in their younger state. This gradually wears off on the larger trees but in saplings it is persistent. The leaves of the White Poplar, introduced from Europe, have a similar cottony lower surface but the teeth are fewer, shallower, and more blunt. The Large-toothed Aspen is largely a tree of the Northeast, but it stretches across lower Canada to Ontario and Minnesota and down the high ground of the Appalachians to Tennessee. Like the Quaking Aspen and the Cottonwood it is found frequently on burnt ground, but it is more persistent and sturdier than the Quaking Aspen and often reaches a respectable age and height of 80 feet or more.

LOMBARDY POPLAR
(*Populus nigra italica*)

We can leave to the botanists the question of where this variety of Poplar originated and why it produces only male catkins. What everybody knows is that untold numbers of Lombardy Poplars line the highways and canal banks of the lowlands of Europe and that the tree is extensively planted for ornamental or other purposes all across temperate North America. If you have a clear view of a Lombardy Poplar, you can recognize it a mile or more away. That's because it is the only broad-leaved tree or non-evergreen that grows in such a narrow, upright fashion. It has a tall, straight trunk and numerous branches that, reaching outward but little, curve sharply upward to parallel the trunk. The appearance of the tree as a whole is that of a towering column of shimmering greenery in Summer and bare branches in Winter.

If anything more than the shape were needed to identify the Lombardy Poplar, the leaf would do it. It has the typical long stalk or "petiole" of the Poplar group but the leaf blade is a triangle, broader than it is high. The leaves vary in size but if the blade is 2½ inches high, it probably will be more than 3 inches in width near the base. Since the tree bears no female catkins, it produces no seed, but that's a small matter because the roots send up shoots—a common custom among Poplars—that are easily cut and planted to start a new generation on its way skyward.

This tree often escapes from cultivation and, with its habit of sending up numerous shoots, it sometimes gets beyond control and becomes a local nuisance. But in its proper place it can be a useful and artistic addition to a landscape. Veterans of European campaigns of the World Wars of modern times will remember the picturesque rows of Lombardy Poplars they so often glimpsed in low, flat country and that gave notice of a road, a river, or a canal in the distance. In the Metropolitan Museum of Art in New York City there is a painting that finds high favor with most visitors, particularly those who love tall trees. It is a canvas by Homer D. Martin showing a row of Lombardy Poplars along the Seine below Paris. The tall trees loom against a blue sky and are reflected in the waters of the river in the foreground. The artist called it "View on the Seine" but the more popular name for it is "Harp of the Winds."

BUTTERNUT
(*Juglans cinerea*)

The badge of the Butternut, of course, is the roughly oblong or football-shaped nut 1½ to 2½ inches long with a velvety but sticky covering. The nuts may be seen clinging to the branchlets when the leaves fall in early Autumn or may be found on the ground under the tree. Aside from that, the Butternut is a medium-sized tree that branches in a somewhat aimless manner and often loses limbs in strong winds. You rarely find Butternut trees of upright character, noble bearing, and fine foliage. Most of them look shiftless in shape and attitude and appear to be merely loitering where they grow. The bark is brownish-gray with straggling vertical grooves in it, and the rather sparse foliage, light green at first, turns yellowish in a vague way as Summer progresses. The trees are never strong and usually linger out a comparatively short life in a crippled condition. The nuts are delicious if it doesn't bother you to have your fingers deeply stained in removing the husk to get at the meat of the matter.

What makes the Butternut of special interest at this point is that it has compound leaves and is the first such tree to be met in this book, though there are many in the woods. In describing the Larch (Page 13), it was explained that a "deciduous" tree is one that loses its leaves in Autumn and, after standing bare all Winter, comes out with a new full crop of leaves in Spring. Roughly speaking, a leaf is the part that falls off a deciduous tree in Autumn. There will remain a "leaf scar" at the parting point and a bud formed there for the production of the shoots of the following year. The Butternut leaf in the picture might seem to be a group of leaves to a beginner, but it is a single leaf made up of a number of divisions called "leaflets" growing opposite one another along a central axis. This arrangement is called "pinnate" and the Butternut leaf is "pinnately compound," from 15 to 30 inches long, with 7 to 17 leaflets from 2 to 4½ inches long and, curiously enough, shaped somewhat like the nuts in outline. The Butternut is found in rich woods, on open slopes, in pastures, and along roadsides over most of temperate North America east of the Rockies.

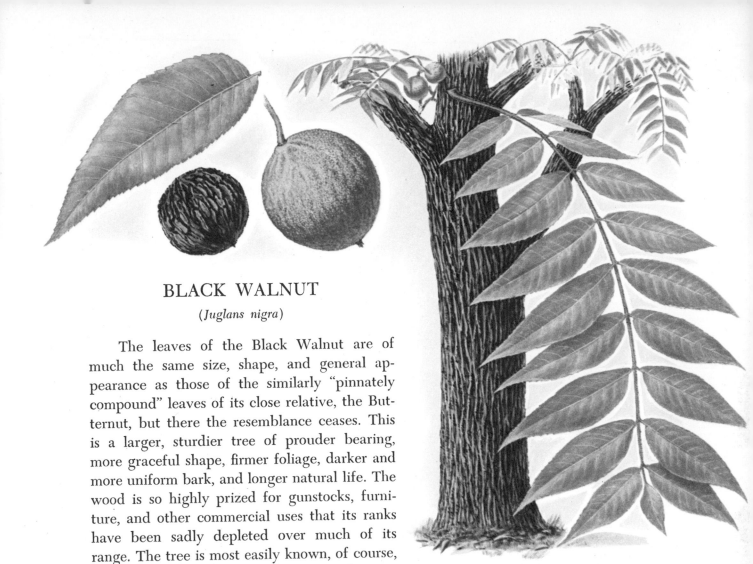

BLACK WALNUT

(Juglans nigra)

The leaves of the Black Walnut are of much the same size, shape, and general appearance as those of the similarly "pinnately compound" leaves of its close relative, the Butternut, but there the resemblance ceases. This is a larger, sturdier tree of prouder bearing, more graceful shape, firmer foliage, darker and more uniform bark, and longer natural life. The wood is so highly prized for gunstocks, furniture, and other commercial uses that its ranks have been sadly depleted over much of its range. The tree is most easily known, of course, by the nuts enclosed in the spherical green husks about 1½ or 2 inches in diameter. These fruits may appear singly or in clusters of twos and threes. The husk is firm and smooth and quite different from the sticky, hairy, wrinkled husk of the Butternut, but it will give the same iodine-like stain to your fingers if you pull it apart to get at the approximately spherical and roughly ridged nut inside. The meat is delicious, but the shell is so thick and hard that it's no easy matter to come at it, which is why the English or Persian Walnut *(Juglans regia)* with its much thinner shell and larger meat content is the species cultivated by the nut growers of the warmer parts of the United States.

The compound leaf of the Black Walnut is from 1 to 2 feet in length and the 11 to 23 leaflets, 2 to 5 inches long. The leaflets are often lopsided at the base and you will note that the sharpening toward the tip is more gradual than it is in the leaflets of the Butternut. The Black Walnut is a hardy tree that is found in the wild from Massachusetts to Minnesota and southward to the higher ground of the Gulf States. In the Southwest and in California there are some other native species of Walnut that may be recognized as such by the resemblance in fruit and leaf to the larger, better-known, more widespread and much more useful Black Walnut that stands as a family favorite in many a farm pasture or rural dooryard.

BITTERNUT HICKORY

(Carya cordiformis)

If you live east of the Mississippi, you probably can find half a dozen species of Hickory in your home territory. They are an eastern group as a whole, though some species are found well west of "the Father of Waters" and Texas has a good assortment. All the Hickories have compound leaves of much similar pattern and produce more or less edible nuts. Staminate and pistillate flowers appear on the same tree after the leaves in Spring, the staminate or male flowers as catkins in drooping clusters of threes, and the pistillate or female flowers in little spikes along the branchlets above. The Hickories are distinguished, one from the other, by easily noted differences in leaves, buds, bark, and the nuts they bear. The Bitternut is one of the most widespread of the group and is found high and low, in wet ground or dry, in open fields or in woods, from Maine across Ontario and Michigan to Minnesota and south to the Gulf States.

The compound leaf of the Bitternut is fairly typical of the clan. The leaflets are sharply toothed in a small way, are practically "sessile" or sitting tight along the leaf axis, and increase in size toward the terminal leaflet. The Bitternut leaves are from 6 to 10 inches long and usually have 7 or 9 leaflets, shaped as shown. The nuts are about 1 inch in diameter and, though the husks fall away readily and the shells are not hard to crack, the contents have a flavor that has fairly earned the name of Bitternut for this species.

Even the beginner will not have much trouble in distinguishing the Bitternut from other Hickories. For one thing, all through the leafless season the Bitternut flaunts bright yellow buds to the Winter winds, a gay touch of color displayed by no other native Hickory. Another difference is that the bark of the Bitternut is much smoother than that of its close relatives. It's a clear, smooth gray bark lined with vertical blackish streaks interwoven in an attractive pattern. On older trees it eventually becomes ridged in a mild way. The Bitternut is an abundant and hardy tree, and a rapid grower that may reach a height of 100 feet, but as lumber it doesn't have the toughness of others of the clan.

SHAGBARK HICKORY

(*Carya ovata*)

The outstanding feature of this tall and stalwart tree is the shaggy bark that explains the common name by which it is known over a range that extends from Quebec and Maine across Ontario to North Dakota and south to the Gulf Coast region. The only other native tree with somewhat similar bark is the Big Shellbark Hickory (*Carya laciniosa*) that is found over about half of the same range. Where the two species grow in the same area there are differences in bark and leaf that are easily noted. For instance, the bark on the trunk of this species seems to be more "at loose ends," so to speak. The rather broad, ragged, plates of gray bark of the Shagbark curl away from the trunk at the edges, particularly the lower end. The longer and narrower loose strips of the Big Shellbark do not flare out in that fashion. Another point of difference is that the compound leaves of the Shagbark, 8 to 20 inches long, usually have only 5 leaflets, as shown in the illustration, whereas the larger leaves of the Big Shellbark, 12 to 24 inches long, usually have 7 leaflets. The fruit runs to the same scale. Husk and all, they may be 2 or 2¼ inches in diameter, with the Big

Shellbark products averaging just a bit the larger. The husks are thick and the shells of the nuts are hard to crack, but it's worth the trouble because the flavor of the meat is delicious.

Hickory lumber is noted for its toughness and the Shagbark furnished much of the wood that was turned into spokes for wheels when wagons were the common carriers of goods and passengers in this country. It is now much in demand for the handles of axes and other tools. The wood is heavy, even for a Hickory, and a cubic foot of it, dried, weighs just a bit over 52 pounds. It shares with some others of the Hickory clan the honor of being used as firewood in the production of "hickory-smoked hams" and other such delicacies. If you come across this tree in Winter, note the large, cream-colored terminal buds with the darker "bud scales" that protect them. There are numerous other Hickories native to this continent, but you can sort them out in time by taking note of the details of bark, bud, and fruit and the size, shape, and number of the leaflets of the compound leaves.

PECAN
(Carya illinoensis)

This is the largest of our native Hickories and there are reports of trees in the wild up to 160 feet in height, with tremendous trunks and a wide crown of foliage. Originally an inhabitant of the lowlands of the Mississippi Basin, it is now cultivated well beyond its natural range for the commercial value of the thin-shelled, oblong-cylindrical nuts of fine flavor that it bears in abundance. The compound leaves are from 9 to 20 inches in length, with 9 to 15 leaflets about 4 inches in length and much alike in shape, thus differing from the other Hickories whose leaflets usually increase much in size and change somewhat in shape toward the outer end of the compound leaf. The nuts, in thin husks that are easily removed, grow in clusters of 3 to 11 and by their shape definitely identify the tree for anyone who may be in doubt.

HOP HORNBEAM
(Ostrya virginiana)

This tree, common in hardwood forests over the eastern half of temperate North America, often is overlooked. It never grows to great size and its leaves, 2 to 5 inches long and shaped as shown, are not distinctive. The light-colored fruit clusters, which look like the hops used in brewing and give the tree its name, often are at least partly concealed by the heavy, drooping foliage of late Spring or early Summer. The easiest way to make the acquaintance of the Hop Hornbeam is to look for it in Winter when you will know it by its gray-brown bark seemingly fashioned of papery vertical strips, its many long, thin, drooping branchlets and, at the tips of many of the branchlets, clusters of 2 or 3 tiny staminate catkins held stiffly at divergent angles. These Winter catkins, about ¾ inch long, expand and droop, as shown, in Spring to furnish the pollen to fertilize the female flowers that come with the unfolding of the leaves.

[30]

HORNBEAM; IRONWOOD; BLUE BEECH
(*Carpinus caroliniana*)

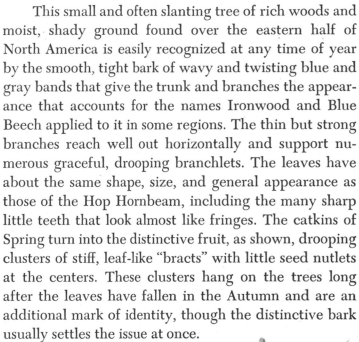

This small and often slanting tree of rich woods and moist, shady ground found over the eastern half of North America is easily recognized at any time of year by the smooth, tight bark of wavy and twisting blue and gray bands that give the trunk and branches the appearance that accounts for the names Ironwood and Blue Beech applied to it in some regions. The thin but strong branches reach well out horizontally and support numerous graceful, drooping branchlets. The leaves have about the same shape, size, and general appearance as those of the Hop Hornbeam, including the many sharp little teeth that look almost like fringes. The catkins of Spring turn into the distinctive fruit, as shown, drooping clusters of stiff, leaf-like "bracts" with little seed nutlets at the centers. These clusters hang on the trees long after the leaves have fallen in the Autumn and are an additional mark of identity, though the distinctive bark usually settles the issue at once.

BLACK, SWEET, or CHERRY BIRCH
(*Betula lenta*)

To the ordinary observer and for practical purposes most of our Birches are distinguished one from the other by the color of the bark. Thus we have White, Gray, Red, Yellow, and Black Birches, as well as a few other less common Birches of narrower range. The Black Birch has dark bark somewhat similar to that of the Cherry Tree, which accounts for another of its common names, but Sweet Birch is a logical name for it. This is the tree with the strong wintergreen flavor from root to branchlet. If you lay the axe to a Black Birch, the air is fragrant as the chips fly. The tree, which grows to a height of 70 to 80 feet, is common in rich woods from Maine and Quebec to Ontario and southward to the uplands of Georgia and Tennessee. The leaves, shaped as shown, are 2½ to 5 inches long and have fringe-like teeth. Through the Autumn and Winter the bare branchlets carry not only the little upright seed-filled cones or "strobiles" of the season but the pendent and tightly sealed staminate catkins that, through whirling snows and icy blasts, wait patiently for the warm summons of returning Spring.

[31]

YELLOW BIRCH
(*Betula lutea*)

This is much like the Black Birch in leaf, branch, and fruit, but the yellowish sheen to the rather loose and laterally peeling bark on the trunk makes it easy to recognize the Yellow Birch in the woods. You might even think that the bark had been lightly buttered here and there. There are minor differences in the leaves and fruit of the Black and Yellow Birch but, to a beginner, the resemblances will be more easily noted than the differences. The Yellow Birch twigs even have a pleasant wintergreen flavor, though to a lesser degree than the Black Birch twigs. On the average, this is a larger tree than the Black Birch and it likes higher and cooler territory. It is found from Quebec to Minnesota and southward on high ground to North Carolina and Tennessee. The seed "cones," like those of the Black Birch, hang on for months and provide food for many birds in Winter.

RED BIRCH; RIVER BIRCH
(*Betula nigra*)

At first sight a beginner might mistake a Red Birch for a Yellow Birch because of the shaggy, peeling bark, but in this species the tint is red instead of yellow and the curling patches are smaller and more numerous upward along the trunk. If in doubt, look at the leaves. The leaf blades of the Yellow Birch, like those of the Black Birch, are well rounded or even "scalloped" or heart-shaped at the base, while those of the Yellow Birch start out at an angle away from the base. Some call them "diamond-shaped," but that's going a little too far. A still more helpful matter to the beginner is that the Red Birch and Yellow Birch do not commonly mix with one another. Between them they cover the whole eastern half of temperate North America from the Gulf States well into Canada, but the Red Birch is the southerly species and the Yellow the northerly resident. Where their ranges overlap the Yellow Birch is on high ground and the Red Birch on low ground, often on river banks, which accounts for its secondary name of River Birch. The leaves of the Red Birch, as you will note, are more coarsely toothed than those of the Yellow Birch. The seed "cones" ripen in June and fall away quickly.

WHITE BIRCH; PAPER BIRCH

(*Betula papyrifera*)

This is one of the most striking and beautiful trees in North America. It prefers a cool climate and its natural range is the high ground in the northerly section of the United States and northward to the Arctic Circle. It grows to be a fairly tall tree and it stands out in the woods because of the contrast in color between its white bark and the dark bark of the surrounding trees. There are very few native trees with which it could possibly be confused, even at a distance. One is the Sycamore, whose upper limbs sometimes have a clear cream-white bark that catches the eye from far away; but the Sycamore rarely invades the cool northerly region in which the White Birch flourishes, and in the few areas where they may be found on common ground, it is no problem at all to distinguish one from the other on closer inspection. The mottled trunk of the Sycamore is nothing like the clear white trunk of this tree and there are, of course, notable differences in leaf, flower, and fruit.

But Gray Birch and White Birch often are confused by novices in the woods. Both trees are Birches with white bark, so there is some ground for confusion at first sight. There are, however, two details that easily distinguish one species from the other. The leaves of the Gray Birch are decidedly triangular in outline with the stalk or "petiole" in the middle of the flat base line. The White Birch leaves, 1 to 4 inches long, are shaped, as shown, with the base line of the leaf blade gently curving away on each side of the petiole. But leaves often vary in shape and if there is any doubt in your mind about the identity of the tree, rub your hand over the white bark of the trunk. If it is a Gray Birch, your hand will come away clean. If it's a White Birch, the palm of your hand will be covered with a white powdery substance that coats the bark and adds a final velvety touch to its beauty. The handsome bark of this species peels laterally in strips and discloses a lovely red-brown or sometimes fawn-colored inner bark. Outer and inner bark were used by the Indians in the making of canoes and in more modern times they have been fashioned into writing paper, picture frames, and souvenirs of all kinds. You may occasionally encounter other white-barked Birches, native or imported, but this and the Gray Birch are by far the most common. Learn them first.

GRAY BIRCH
(*Betula populifolia*)

This is the small Birch that springs up in great numbers in neglected fields and burned-over areas and on embankments and filled ground in the northeastern section of the United States and adjacent Canada. It is rarely more than 30 feet in height, pyramidal in its younger days but usually slim and slanting if it survives to grow more than 20 feet tall. It has thin, drooping branchlets; the triangular leaves that distinguish it from the true White Birch are lustrous and long-petioled, and they shimmer and waver in light breezes like those of the Quaking Aspen. The white bark of this tree does not peel in the manner of the White Birch and the trunk is marked with triangular dark patches, particularly beneath the branching points. It's a tree of fast growth and is very common over its range, but its range is narrow, its life is short, and it is often crippled by ice storms.

COMMON ALDER
(*Alnus serrulata*)

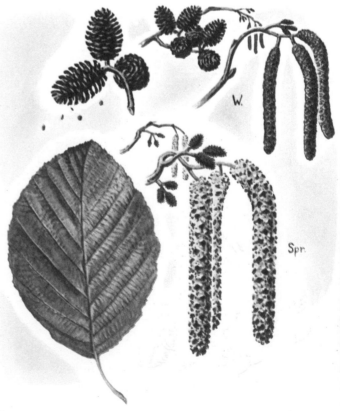

The Alders are a group of shrubs and trees closely related to the Birches, as may be noted by the catkins and fruiting cones or "strobiles" they produce and which, remaining on the leafless branches in Winter, serve as an easy guide in becoming acquainted with them. That is, you will find it an easy matter to know an Alder when you see one, but which species is a matter to be taken up later with more experience. On the Pacific Coast the Red Alder may be a tree 90 feet tall, but in the East most of the Alders are shrubs like the much-branched Common Alder whose leaves, catkins, and fruiting cones are shown here. This species, which grows to 15 feet or more in height, is found in swamps and wet ground generally from Nova Scotia south to Florida and southwestward to Oklahoma.

[34]

BEECH

(*Fagus grandifolia*)

You can't mistake a Beech if you see one, and it is common in the woods over most of the eastern half of the United States and adjacent Canada. Furthermore, it has been extensively planted for decorative purposes and you may find it flourishing almost anywhere in temperate North America. The clear, smooth, tight-fitting, light gray bark of the trunk and branches of the Beech is as well known as the red breast of the Robin. A mature Beech is tall, broad, handsome, and useful. The wood is used for furniture, tool handles, salad bowls and many other purposes. Beechnuts are on the diet list of many birds and mammals. They were the favorite food of the immense flocks of Passenger Pigeons that, we are told, "darkened the skies" as they flew over this country a century ago and have since vanished from the face of the earth. Of the countless millions of Passenger Pigeons that once were found in North America, no single descendant survives.

Beeches tend to form groves in many localities but they also are found interspersed with other trees such as Oaks, Maples, Birches, and Ashes in mixed forests. The leaves are 3 to 6 inches long, shaped as shown, with prominent veins and sharp teeth that are really the outer ends of the veins. If you look carefully just after the leaves unfold in Spring, you

will find the inconspicuous flowers. The staminate or male flowers hang in a fluffy cluster on a thin stalk 1 inch or more in length and the pistillate or female flowers appear in stubby, upright clusters along the branchlets. The beechnuts are something like miniature chestnuts in their bristle-covered, short-stalked little husks that eventually open from the outer end and drop the tasty fruit to the ground below, where it is found and deeply appreciated by many forms of wildlife. In the Winter, looking at the long, thin, sharp-pointed buds of the Beech, you will understand Thoreau's reference to them as "the spearheads of Spring." The Copper Beech so often seen in cultivation is a color variety of the European Beech, which closely resembles our native species but has a bark darker in tone. Nurserymen also have developed a Weeping Beech and several other varieties. But all these are easily recognized as Beeches by those who know our native Beech. Look in Beech groves for Beechdrops, stiff, brown-stalked flowering plants parasitic on Beech roots.

[35]

CHESTNUT

(*Castanea dentata*)

From Maine to Minnesota and southward on high ground to Florida and Mississippi, the children of today have been deprived of a birthright. Long ago over the same area there was no finer sport for youngsters than to go hunting for chestnuts on a crisp Autumn morning when frost had opened the big burs with the fierce prickles on the outside and the rose-velvet lining on the inside. The opened burs above meant that there were chestnuts to be found below. Searching in the grass and among the fallen leaves was a great game in which there was competition for quality as well as quantity in treasure-trove. "Oh, boy! Look at this one!" "Bet I find a bigger one!" They were shining brown, silky, and beautiful. You could eat them on the spot or take them home and serve them up boiled, roasted, or mashed. The flavor was delicious whether they were raw or cooked.

If youngsters prized the tree for the nut crop it produced, lumbermen looked on the Chestnut with high favor for other reasons. It provided wood of the finest kind for many commercial purposes and it was rich in the tannin used in the tanning industry. In the open, it was a stalwart tree with a broad crown. Some pasture Chestnuts were 80 feet or more in height and about as broad as they were tall. But the almost incredible fact is that the great Chestnut trees that flourished so widely in this country only a half-century ago

have vanished, every last one of them! "Going for chestnuts" of an October morning on a hillside bright with Autumn foliage is no longer a radiant reality but a fond memory of days that are no more.

What happened was that an imported fungus struck the trees at their tops and slowly crept downward, killing them inch by inch while scientists tried in vain to halt the slaughter. From the roots of the gaunt skeletons came numerous shoots but, when such shoots became saplings 15 to 20 feet tall, the blight cut them down. To this day the deceptive cycle goes on and often you will find, springing from old roots, Chestnut saplings bearing leaves, as shown, 6 to 9 inches long, with pin-point teeth that distinguish them from Oak leaves of similar size and shape. You might even find saplings with golden, flowering plumes or possibly a few burs. If so, gaze upon them fondly. These saplings are the Peter Pans of the tree world. Our joy in them is mixed with sadness. They can never grow up.

WHITE OAK

(Quercus alba)

*Then here's to the Oak, the brave old
Oak,
Who stands in his pride alone!
And still flourish he, a hale green tree,
When a hundred years are gone!*
(H. F. Chorley, 1808–72.)

Oaks are mighty trees with virtues that have been enshrined in mottoes, maxims, and proverbs. "Tall Oaks from little acorns grow." "Little strokes fell great Oaks." "Strong as an Oak." "Hearts of Oak." There are Oaks in all pleasant lands north of the Equator and there are dozens of species in North America. Furthermore, they hybridize in a way to puzzle the expert at times, which means that a beginner can lose his way among the Oaks in no time at all. However, a start can be made by learning how to recognize some of the more common species of different regions of this continent.

Our native Oaks seem to fall naturally into two divisions called the White Oaks and the Black (or, if you prefer, Red) Oaks. The important or scientific distinction is that the species in the White Oak group have flowers that produce acorns in a single season. In the Black Oak group the acorns are not "full grown" or "ripe" until the second year of their existence. The unimportant but very helpful difference to the beginner among trees is that, as a rule, the ends of the veins of the leaves in the Black Oak group stick out as harmless spines or tiny, hair-like bristles.

Look at the leaves of this White Oak. There are many lobes, but not a bristle tip at the end of any one of them. Of course, that quick test at a glance merely tells the beginner that the leaf puts the tree either in the White Oak or the Black (or Red) Oak group. Tracking down the species is more difficult and often requires a study of three kinds of evidence; the bark, the leaf and the acorn. The difference in bark often is hard to discern and leaves are quite variable in size and shape. The best evidence is the acorn. The White Oak is one of the tall, broad, and brawny trees of the forests of North America from the Atlantic Coast to the foothills of the Rockies. The leaves are variable but usually they have 5 to 7 deep lobes and are 4 to 9 inches in length. The cylindrical acorns are about ¾ inch in length and the cup is quite shallow, covering only the lower quarter or third of the acorn. These are the details to note when tracking down any species of Oak. The staminate flowers of the Oaks, hanging in drooping catkins, are much visited by insect-seeking warblers on Spring migration.

[37]

MOSSY-CUP OAK; BUR OAK
(Quercus macrocarpa)

This shows how helpful the acorn can be in identifying the Oaks. Where you find a large, roundish acorn deeply set in a broad, gray, heavily beaded cup with an astonishing silvery fringe at the rim, you will know immediately that you have come upon a Mossy-cup or Bur Oak. These striking cups may be as much as 2 inches in width, but 1¼ inches would be about average. You might note that the leaves are deeply lobed near the base and broader and more solid toward the tip, but the acorns are as good as a signboard on the tree. The Mossy-cup Oak ranges from Nova Scotia to Manitoba and south to Texas, but it is not common in the Northeast and is rarely found on the Atlantic Coastal Plain south of Delaware. It flourishes best in the river basins of the interior and is said to reach a height of 150 feet or more in the Wabash Valley. Its ability to withstand the cold Winters of Manitoba proves that it is one of the hardiest of our Oaks.

CHESTNUT OAK; ROCK OAK
(Quercus prinus)

A glance at the leaf will tell you why this is called the Chestnut Oak but you can see that the wavy teeth of this leaf are blunt or rounded and quite unlike the sharp teeth of the Chestnut leaf. The name Rock Oak, applied to it in some areas, is due to its fondness for rocky slopes over a range that extends from Maine to upland Georgia, with a scattering representation from Ontario and Michigan south to the Ohio Valley. The acorns are about 1 inch long, narrowly oval, and one third to one half enclosed in a thin cup. This is an Oak of only medium height but it grows to a great age and on older trees the heavy vertical ridges on the lower part of the trunk help to identify the species. The beginner must be warned, however, that there are other Oaks with somewhat similar leaves and acorns and even the botanists are not in complete agreement as to how they should be separated and named. This species is offered as a sample of the group.

LIVE OAK

(*Quercus virginiana*)

This cherished tree of the Deep South is found from Virginia down the Atlantic Coastal Plain into Florida and across the Gulf Coast region into Texas and Mexico. It is rarely more than 50 feet in height, but where it grows in the open it carries a widespread crown of shining foliage and the horizontal reach of some of the branches is remarkable. It is called Live Oak because the lustrous leaves remain on the tree through the Winter and do not drop off until the new crop is coming along in Spring. Thus it has a "live" appearance when other Oaks seem "dead" in their leafless Winter sleep. The unlobed leaves are mostly narrowly oval in shape and from 1 to 4 inches long, but they vary considerably in shape and size in different regions. The dark acorns, shaped as shown, and up to 1 inch in length, are borne on longish stalks or "peduncles" with from 1 to 5 acorns in a cluster. There are other Oaks with unlobed leaves but the species can be sorted out by leaf and acorn details.

COAST LIVE OAK

(*Quercus agrifolia*)

The comparatively few native "live" or evergreen Oaks are inhabitants of the warmer sections of North America. The Emory Oak (*Quercus emoryi*) of the Southwest, the aptly named Canyon Live Oak (*Quercus chrysolepis*) of the mountain valleys from Oregon to Mexico, and the Coast Live Oak whose holly-like leaves and bullet-shaped acorns are shown

here, are three such species. All of them have unlobed leaves, usually with spiny teeth, but each may be distinguished by the size and shape of the leaves and acorns. The Coast Live Oak is found along the coastal area from San Francisco southward into Lower California. Where the sea winds whip it with salt spray on exposed headlands it is stunted and scraggly, but on inland hillsides or the forested uplands it grows to a height of 80 or 90 feet with widespread branches. The leaves are from 1 to 4 inches long and the curious acorns vary from ¾ inch to 1½ inches in length. The California White Oak (*Quercus lobata*) has somewhat similar acorns even longer and thinner than these, but the deeply and bluntly lobed leaves bear no resemblance to those of this species.

[39]

RED OAK
(*Quercus rubra*)

This is truly one of the great trees of field and forest over most of the eastern half of the United States and adjacent Canada. It is among the tallest of our native Oaks and probably the hardiest of that stalwart clan. It ventures well into Canada, farther north than most Oaks of this continent, and flourishes in regions where the snows are deep, the winds icy, and the temperature readings low for many months of the year. It is a fast grower and seldom is bothered by blight or insect pests. It bears acorns in profusion and, because they have a bitter taste that causes squirrels and other animals to neglect them as an article of diet, they remain on the ground to produce saplings in great numbers. For these and other reasons the Red Oak is one of the most common Oaks over its range. It averages 70 to 80 feet in height at maturity, usually has a stout trunk clear of branches for some distance above the ground, and is one of the most valuable timber trees of North America. It is also a fine shade tree whose worth is appreciated not only in this country but in Europe where it has been planted more extensively than any other native American Oak.

Such are some of the virtues of this tall, strong, and handsome tree. There are varying explanations of how it came by the name of Red Oak. Some say it's because of the reddish inner bark. Others think the name refers to the reddish twigs, the red tinge to the leaves as they unfold in the Spring, or the deep red color they turn in the Autumn. You can tell from the typical leaves shown above that there is considerable variation in its foliage. Saplings sometimes have enormous leaves but on mature trees the many-lobed, bristle-tipped leaves are 4 to 8 inches long, deep green above and yellowish-green underneath. There are other Oaks with somewhat similar leaves but note that the shape of the Red Oak leaf is broadly oval and that the clefts of the lobes, at the deepest, are well out from the midrib. But Oak leaves are tricky in many species and, on the average, the acorn is a better clue. The Red Oak acorn, shaped as shown, is about 1 inch long. As you can see, it's a fine stout acorn set in a particularly shallow cup. There is no other acorn like it over most of the range of the Red Oak.

BLACK OAK

(Quercus velutina)

Most persons refer to this species as the Black Oak but it also is known as the Yellow Oak, the Yellow-barked Oak and the Quercitron Oak in different parts of the country. You can take your choice or follow local option but, to simplify matters, it will be called the Black Oak here. It is one of our tallest Oaks and a common one over much the same range as that of the Red Oak except that the Red Oak extends further in a northerly direction and the Black Oak goes all the way down to the Gulf Coast, which the Red Oak does not. The many-lobed, bristle-tipped leaves of this species vary greatly in shape and size, even on the same tree. On mature trees they may be anything from 3 to 12 inches in length, some of them deeply cleft between narrow lobes, others with narrow clefts between broad lobes, and still others with only shallow indentations like the lower leaf in the illustration. In general, however, they tend to be "heavy-headed" or obovate in outline, broader beyond the middle than toward the base, and deeply lobed.

The acorns are the most reliable guide in tracking down this species. They aren't much to look at but they run fairly true to form. Shaped as shown, they average about ⅝ inch in length and not much less than that in width. Note that the cup covers half or more of the acorn and is "raspy" around the rim. Another feature of this species is the yellow inner bark that furnishes tannin for use in the tanning of leather and a yellow dye used in the textile industry.

There are some sixty or so species of native Oak in North America and a few introduced species including the Cork Oak (*Quercus suber*) of the Mediterranean area whose spongy inner bark furnishes the corks for bottles. Maples, Elms, Birches, and other such groups have leaves that run somewhat to a general pattern for the group. But not the Oaks! They display leaves in an astonishing assortment of shapes and sizes. Even the general rule that bristle-tipped leaves indicate Oaks that take two years to ripen their acorns is merely a "rule of thumb" that doesn't hold in the case of the Coast Live Oak and a few other species that have spiny-tipped leaves and ripen their acorns in a single season. But these variations in size and shape of leaves, along with the acorns, help to track down the different Oaks.

PIN OAK

(*Quercus palustris*)

This is an Oak of medium size that is more or less common in lowlands and moist ground generally, from Massachusetts to Iowa and south to North Carolina and Oklahoma. The bark is dark and, for an Oak, rather smooth and tight-fitting. The leaves are 4 to 6 inches long and deeply lobed, and the acorns are delightfully neat little things in flat cups, shaped as shown, and about ½ inch long or broad. The bristle tips of the leaves show it to be one of the Black (or Red) Oak group. The name Pin Oak comes from its numerous slender branchlets. The *palustris* in its scientific name comes from the Latin word for a swamp and refers to its fondness for wet ground, but it is a sturdy tree and can live in dry ground if planted there. The slender branchlets and the drooping curve of many of its branches make this an Oak that can be recognized as far as it can be seen in the leafless season. The small leaves, the slender branchlets, and the neat little acorns are the marks of the Pin Oak.

SLIPPERY ELM

(*Ulmus rubra*)

This is the Elm with the savory and slippery inner bark that is turned into lozenges for the drugstore trade. It grows throughout most of the eastern half of temperate North America but is usually passed over as "just another Elm" by the ordinary wayfarer. However, if you look closely, you may recognize it by the large leaves that are covered on the upper surface with hairs that are stiff to the touch no matter which way you rub your fingers over them. They are typical Elm leaves, alternate on the branchlets, sharp-toothed, and lopsided at the base, as shown, but they are 4 to 8 inches long, which is above average for Elms. The seed "wafers" of other native Elms have a fringe of tiny hairs around the rim but the Slippery Elm does not. In the Winter a good mark of the Slippery Elm is the covering of long rusty hairs on the dark oval buds that stand out along the gray twigs. But the sad truth is that this tree is safe only when it goes unrecognized.

AMERICAN ELM

(Ulmus americana)

The original range of this lovely tree of classic shape and graceful bearing extended only from the Atlantic Coast to the foothills of the Rockies, but it has been so extensively planted that it now may be found in abundance everywhere in temperate North America. It's a tree of the wild that has become almost domesticated by popular demand. It's a delight in our dooryards and a solace in our cemeteries. It ornaments our public parks. It stands as guardian of our city streets and as warden of our village greens. Go for an auto ride almost anywhere in this country and most of the Oaks, Maples, Pines, Hickories, and other trees that you see along the way will be growing where the seed settled on the soil. But most of the American Elms that you see will be growing where somebody planted them by hand. These trees are truly things of beauty and if not "a joy forever," a joy for at least a century unless the dread Dutch Elm disease gets in its deadly work.

Oliver Wendell Holmes, the genial "Autocrat Of The Breakfast Table," had a great love for the noted Elms of New England and drove many a mile to inspect some famous ones and put his tape measure around their trunks. If you haven't done so, read his account in "The Autocrat" of one such expedition; the hearsay report of a tremendous Elm, the

setting out, the fear of disappointment, the heartthrob at the first distant sight of a swelling crown of foliage, the arrival, and the absolute awe at the grandeur of the great tree! For a tree lover, that is a thrilling adventure story.

The American Elm leaves, shaped and toothed as shown, are 2 to 6 inches long. They average a bit smaller than the leaves of the Slippery Elm, are not as rough to the touch on the upper surface and are more lopsided at the base. The fruiting wafers of this species are slightly smaller than those of the Slippery Elm and they have a fine fringe of tiny hairs around the edges. There are other native Elms and a few imported ones, like the English and Scotch Elms that have been widely planted. All of them have characteristic Elm leaves and fruits but they may be distinguished by differences in leaf, bark, or branches as well as details of flowers and seed "wafers." This species, however, is the loveliest of all.

HACKBERRY; SUGARBERRY

(*Celtis occidentalis*)

We have a number of native species of Hackberry in North America, but this is by far the most widespread and when you have learned to know this one on sight you will have little difficulty recognizing its close relatives. This species may be found from the Atlantic Coast to the Rockies and from the Gulf States to the Canadian Border and even beyond it in Ontario and Quebec, but it isn't fond of cold weather or long Winters and it thins out or disappears at high altitudes and along the northern border of the United States. You will know it by its gray bark curiously ridged or sprinkled with warty growths, its sharply toothed leaves 2 to 5 inches long, shaped as shown, and often studded with light patches caused by a fungus, and by the fruit that accounts for the name of Hackberry or Sugarberry. These berries or "drupes," purple-black when ripe, are about ⅓ inch in diameter.

RED MULBERRY

(*Morus rubra*)

The White Mulberry of Asia, whose leaves are the diet of the silkworm, was planted in the American Colonies in the hope that the silk industry could be fostered here. The tree took root but the silk industry did not. The result is that the White Mulberry is now more common than our native Red Mulberry in some Atlantic States. The Red Mulberry, found from New England across Ontario to the Dakotas and south to the Gulf Coast, is a bigger and better tree in every way. It has larger leaves, much better fruit, and a longer fruiting period much appreciated by many kinds of birds. The White Mulberry crop comes and goes in a couple of weeks but the Red Mulberry carries fruit through many weeks of Summer. On the young shoots you will find the curiously lobed leaves that are a mark of the Mulberry clan. The ordinary heart-shaped leaves are 2 to 6 inches long. If you pluck a leaf, you will see a drop of milky juice appear at the point of separation from the twig; another family trait.

[44]

OSAGE ORANGE; BOWDOCK

(*Maclura pomifera*)

This relative of the Mulberries that can be anything from a much-twisted shrub to a well-rounded tree 60 feet in height has a fruit mass the size and shape of an old-fashioned cannon ball, a feature that leaves no doubt as to its identity when these greenish-yellow spherical objects from 3 to 5 inches in diameter strew the ground underneath the tree in early Autumn or cling to the bare branches after the leaves have fallen. If you break open one of these pebbly-surfaced spheres, you will find it something like a compact cauliflower in texture—but not in taste! Incidentally, in breaking it open, you probably will find your fingers sticky from the milky juice oozing from the cuts or bruises in the vegetable matter. It is not, of course, a single fruit but innumerable fruits joined together to form this lumpy globular mass of seeds and fleshy coverings and attachments. Staminate and pistillate flowers appear on different trees. Since the fruit masses are a picturesque feature of the species, the pistillate or female trees that produce the fruit are preferred for planting. It seems a great waste that the fruit isn't good eating but it is rarely used for food by bird or beast, and no child who has tasted it ever is eager for a second helping.

Aside from the spectacular fruit clusters, the Osage Orange of either sex may be known by the brownish-yellow or orange-yellow bark of the many curving branches, the shining leaves 3 to 5 inches long, shaped as shown in the illustration, the thorns that are a real menace along its branches, and the milky juice that appears where you break off a leaf, a bud, or even a thorn. The milky juice is common to the Mulberry family but the thorns are an added feature in the Osage Orange. It is native to Missouri, Kansas, Oklahoma, Arkansas, Louisiana, and northeastern Texas, but it has been widely spread by cultivation and now may be found almost anywhere in the United States. These trees are frequently planted to form hedges and, if trimmed low, the curving branches with their sharp thorns form an almost impenetrable barrier. The Osage Indians of its native territory extracted a yellow dye from the wood of this tree and also used it to make bows for hunting and warfare. For that reason the early French settlers of Louisiana gave the tree the name of "Bois d'arc" or Bow Wood. In time the French "Bois d'arc" was corrupted to Bowdock, a name that still survives in some areas. Another name for it is Mock Orange, which is unfortunate because that is also a common name for two different species of flowering shrub. Such confusion shows the value of scientific names that remain constant all over the world for all plants and creatures under the sun.

SWAMP MAGNOLIA; SWEET BAY
(*Magnolia virginiana*)

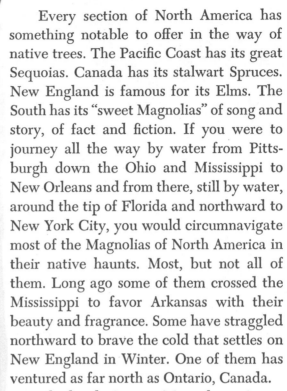

Every section of North America has something notable to offer in the way of native trees. The Pacific Coast has its great Sequoias. Canada has its stalwart Spruces. New England is famous for its Elms. The South has its "sweet Magnolias" of song and story, of fact and fiction. If you were to journey all the way by water from Pittsburgh down the Ohio and Mississippi to New Orleans and from there, still by water, around the tip of Florida and northward to New York City, you would circumnavigate most of the Magnolias of North America in their native haunts. Most, but not all of them. Long ago some of them crossed the Mississippi to favor Arkansas with their beauty and fragrance. Some have straggled northward to brave the cold that settles on New England in Winter. One of them has ventured as far north as Ontario, Canada.

The lovely Swamp Magnolia or Sweet Bay is a tree that reaches a height of 50 to 60 feet in the swamps and lowlands of the South, but it decreases in size northward and is a thin, small tree at the northern limit of its range, which is the Gloucester region of Massachusetts. Some historians say that the original Swamp Magnolias of the Gloucester area were brought from the South by loving hands and planted where they or their descendants have flourished to such an extent that they gave their name to a seaside Summer resort that grew up nearby and is now Magnolia, Massachusetts, a residential area dotted with magnificent homes overlooking the sea. However, the trees are hardy enough to have made their way that far northward without helping hands and probably did.

In the matter of flower and leaf, this is the smallest of our native Magnolias, on which account it is known as the Small Magnolia in some regions. It is also called the Swamp Bay, the Sweet Bay, the Beaver Tree, and the Laurel Magnolia. Its somewhat leathery and narrowly oval leaves are 3 to 6 inches long, shining green above, and a soft whitish-gray underneath that helps to identify the tree when flowers and fruit are missing. The leaves are evergreen in the South, but they go with the Winter winds in the North. The cream-white, cup-shaped flower of 6 to 9 petals is 2 to 3 inches across before the petals sag, and the lumpy red fruiting cone or seed cluster characteristic of the Magnolias is about 1½ inches in length. This species offers a good example of the value of a scientific name for a tree or, in fact, any plant. It has many common names and varies in size from a shrub to a 60-foot tree over its range, but the scientific name remains constant throughout.

CUCUMBER TREE

(Magnolia acuminata)

This member of the Magnolia group owes its common name to the fact that its lumpy fruit in the green stage looks something like a cucumber. This is the hardiest and the tallest of the native Magnolias, reaching a height of 100 feet under favorable conditions and pushing as far north as Canadian ground where the Province of Ontario dips down among the Great Lakes. It is found from that region southward to the Gulf of Mexico and there is no difficulty in distinguishing it from any of the other Magnolias at any time of year because this species has ridged bark on its trunk whereas the other Magnolias have a smooth gray bark somewhat like that of the Beech.

You have to look sharp to find the flowers in late Spring because they are not striking in color and often are concealed by the leaves that, shaped as shown, are rather thin in texture compared to other Magnolias and are 6 to 10 inches long. The flower petals are 2 to 3 inches long and the lumpy cylindrical fruit containing the seeds is about the same length, turning from green to a dull red as it ripens. Eventually the bright red seeds slip out and dangle on thin threads before they fall to the ground, a common trait in the Magnolia clan. The Umbrella Tree (*Magnolia tripetala*), so called because its huge leaves (up to 2 feet long) are clustered around the tips of the branches in umbrella fashion, is cultivated as far north as New England. It is a fine shade tree and has handsome white flowers of good size, but the odor will never be enshrined in perfume and offered for sale in the best shops.

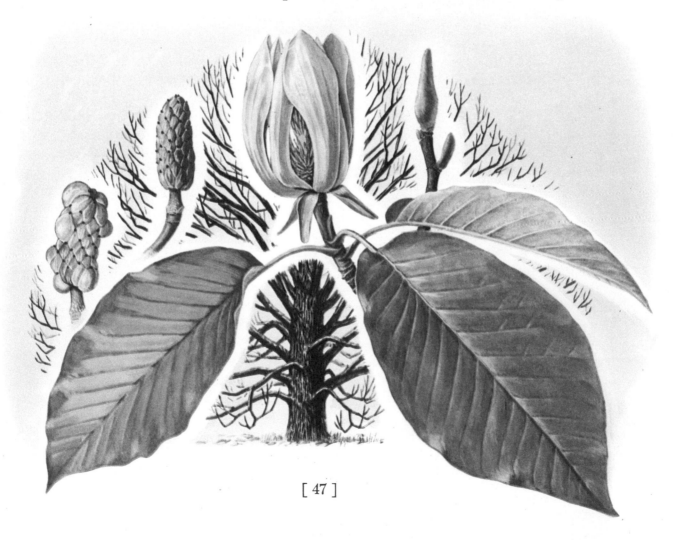

[47]

TULIP TREE
(*Liriodendron tulipifera*)

Here is a tall and stalwart tree that is not only magnificent in bulk but distinctive in almost every particular. It has a trunk like a Greek column, a lovely flower, an odd-shaped leaf, conical clusters of winged seeds that stand out against the cold sky in late Autumn, and reddish-brown Winter buds that look like miniature thumbless leather mittens. The young bark of branches and saplings is smooth and green, but the old bark of the great cylindrical boles of the big trees is deeply fissured and a rich brown in color. By the towering trunk alone you may know the tree. But the leaves, too, are in a class by themselves. We have no other native tree of North America with such square or broadly indented tips, and the way the young leaves unfold in Spring is a delight to watch. They are coiled in the bud and folded along the midrib in such fashion that as they emerge they look like tiny taximeter flags coming to the upright position

If anything else were needed to identify the Tulip Tree, the abundant flowers that cover it during May and June would do it easily. They vary to some extent, but in most of them the basic green of the 6 petals is crossed by a bright orange band with yellow borders. The petals are about 2 inches long and the later conical clusters of winged seeds or "samaras," 2 to 4 inches long, are held upright at the tips of the branches long after the leaves have disappeared. In fact, a few ragged husks may persist until Spring. Purple Finches and other seed-eating birds get some of the tiny seeds with their 1-inch wings but most of them are carried away by the Winter winds. Tulip Trees are found from Rhode Island across southern Massachusetts, New York, and Ontario to Wisconsin and southward to the Gulf Coast region. For some strange reason this tree is called the Yellow Poplar in the lumber industry. The wood is light and is used for such things as crates, boxes, and radio and television cabinets. In late Summer the greenery of the Tulip Tree begins to turn to gold in spots and patches in a way to recall a lovely line by Gerard Manley Hopkins: "Glory be to God for dappled things."

PAWPAW

(*Asimina triloba*)

This shrub or small tree, noted for its odd-looking edible fruit, loves the shade and is found in the undergrowth of woods from New York and Ontario to Nebraska and south to the Gulf Coast. The leaves, shaped as shown, are from 6 to 12 inches long. The showy purple flowers of 6 petals are about 1½ inches in diameter. The fruits, which may be single or 2 or 3 in a cluster, are 3 to 5 inches long and look much like fat little sausages or stubby bananas with rounded ends. They are green at first but turn brown as cool weather ripens them, and the interior contains scattered dark seeds about 1 inch long surrounded by a custard-like sweetish pulp that many persons find delicious. It is often sold in the market. Another way of spelling the name is Papaw and another name for it, a tribute to the fruit, is Custard Apple.

SASSAFRAS

(*Sassafras albidum*)

The legend is that no two leaves of the Sassafras are alike. Of course, that isn't true. Though the leaves are quite variable in shape and size, there are usually enough of the "mit-

ten" type to make it easy to recognize a Sassafras whether it is a sapling a few feet high or a tree 80 or 90 feet tall with a rugged trunk of deeply grooved brown bark. It sprouts so readily that thickets of Sassafras saplings often are found on the roadside or along the edge of a wood. Your sense of smell will help you identify this tree. Root and branch, flower and fruit, all are highly aromatic when crushed or bruised. The pistillate and staminate flower sprays grow on separate trees, and the pistillate turn into the handsome ⅓-inch fruit, as shown, and are eagerly eaten by birds. The branchlets, twigs, and buds are green in Winter. The Sassafras is found from southern Maine across lower Ontario to Iowa and southward to the Gulf Coast region. Sassafras tea was once supposed to cure all ills.

SPICEBUSH

(*Lindera benzoin*)

The best time to become acquainted with the Spicebush is in the early Spring when, in wet woods and thickets and along stream borders from Maine to Michigan and southward to North Carolina and Kansas, it displays countless clusters of waxy little yellow flowers on dark branches still bare of leaves. It is more of a shrub than a tree and usually occurs in clumps in shady moist ground, with the individual stems radiating outward and upward on a slant to a height of 4 to 15 feet or so. The smooth leaves that appear later are 2 to 5 inches long, about half as wide, and tapering at both ends. The fruit, which ripens in late Summer, is a small partially flattened red "drupe," as the botanists call it, enclosing a single stone. You probably will prefer to call it a berry. The real feature of the Spicebush, and a sure means of identification at any time of year, is the delightful citronella-like odor that comes from any part of the plant under pressure.

WITCH-HAZEL

(*Hamamelis virginiana*)

This is the slanting shrub or small tree of shady ground, including the undergrowth of woods over practically the whole of the eastern half of the United States and adjacent Canada, that so often is cut down and ground up to produce the witch hazel of the drugstore trade. It has several other distinctions. The curious flowers of 4 twisting linear petals like tiny yellow ribbons about ¾ inch in length appear in Autumn and hang on the bare branches after the leaves have fallen. The fruit are nutlets in blunt, little ½-inch capsules that do not ripen until the following Autumn and then by contraction they "explode" and fling the tiny nutlets to the ground some distance away. The leaves are variable but usually broadly oval in shape, 2 to 5 inches long, and wavy or bluntly toothed in outline.

[50]

SWEET GUM; BILSTED

(Liquidambar styraciflua)

This is a tall, handsome tree native to and flourishing best in the southeastern portion of North America and in most cases it can be recognized without an upward glance. That is, unless somebody has been around lately cleaning up with a rake. The Sweet Gum, or Bilsted as it is called in many parts of the South, produces numerous green male and female flowers that generally pass unnoticed and an abundance of horny-coated or "beaked" fruiting spheres about 1 inch in diameter that can't be ignored. These globular clusters of seed capsules dangle from the branchlets on thin stalks or "peduncles" long after the leaves have fallen, and eventually fall themselves to litter the ground as dry brown husks with deep pits where the seeds have disappeared from their cells. There the husks lie until they rot away, which is not a rapid process. On a well-kept lawn, of course, measures have to be taken, usually with a rake and a bushel basket.

When the tree is in foliage it is easily recognized by the long-petioled leaves with blades that are about 6 inches in diameter and star-shaped in outline. On many Sweet Gum trees the smaller branches have corky "wings" or ridges running along them, but this is an individual matter. Some trees display no such ridges on their branchlets and others have them in astonishing abundance. The name Sweet Gum is due to a sticky substance, said to be pleasant to chew, that oozes from cuts made in the trunk or branches. With its attractive gray bark, its distinctive leaves that turn a beautiful combination of crimson and orange in Autumn, and the persistent seed clusters that furnish fine food for Goldfinches, Pine Siskins, Bob-whites, and other birds, the Sweet Gum is an admired and cherished tree over its natural range from the Gulf Coast north to Missouri and Illinois and northeastward to New York and southern New England. You may find it elsewhere under cultivation but it can't stand long periods of low temperature and ordinarily is not hardy as far north as the Canadian Border. It is lumbered for its light, strong wood used in making furniture.

[51]

Spr.

SYCAMORE; BUTTONWOOD; PLANE TREE
(*Platanus occidentalis*)

The most colorful feature of this high, wide, and handsome tree is the bark. A short distance above ground the pebbly brown bark on the massive bole of a big Sycamore becomes a mottled, dappled, or piebald combination of rich brown and cream-white patches, with here and there a splash of pale green. This picturesque pattern extends out some distance along the larger branches, but on the smaller branches the bark is so light in color that, where it shows through the greenery of Summer, the branches look as though they had been whitewashed. This is one of the largest of our native broad-leaved trees and it may reach a height of 150 feet or more under favorable conditions. Over its natural range, which extends from southern Maine across Ontario to Nebraska and south to the Gulf States, it prefers the open country to the forests and the lowlands to the uplands. It flourishes best along natural waterways and the towering masses of foliage and shining branches of rows of great Sycamores often mark the windings of rivers of the rolling regions of the Midwest.

The large, handsome leaves might be mistaken, at a quick glance, for the foliage of some of the Maples, but there are some differences that are immediately noted. In the first place, the Sycamore leaves grow alternately along the branchlets and not opposite one another as do the leaves of all Maples. In the second place, you will see that the swollen base of the leaf stalk or "petiole" is a hollow cap for the bud of next season that will be uncovered when the leaf drops to the ground in Autumn. The leaf blades, lobed and toothed as shown, are 4 to 9 inches in diameter. The little clusters of staminate and pistillate flowers that appear just after the leaves unfold in Spring usually escape notice, but the spherical brown seed clusters, about 1 inch in diameter, dangle on wiry stalks from the bare branches for all to see through the Autumn and Winter. The California Sycamore usually has 2 to 5 seed balls on each hanging stalk. The imported London Plane Tree, much planted in our parks, generally has 2 on a single stalk. Otherwise, these trees look much alike to the ordinary eye.

AMERICAN MOUNTAIN ASH

(Pyrus americana)

These small trees, more often seen in cultivation than in the wild, are easily identified by the compound leaves, the sprays of white flowers in Spring, and the fruit clusters that often cling to the bare branches well into the Winter. The species pictured here is found as a large shrub or small tree from Newfoundland to Manitoba, seeping down into the United States from Maine to Minnesota and running down the high ground of the Appalachians to Georgia and Tennessee. The only difficulty for the beginner is that a more northern species (*Pyrus decora*) and the European Mountain Ash (*Pyrus aucuparia*) look much like this one and may be encountered over much of the same territory. However, the three species may be sorted out later by noticeable differences in the details of flowers, leaves, fruit, and buds. In this species the leaves are about 10 inches long with 11 to 17 leaflets, and the decorative fruits, highly prized for food by many birds and some animals, are about ⅕ inch in diameter.

SERVICEBERRY; SHADBUSH

(Amelanchior arborea)

It might help the beginner to know that the scientific name of this species means "tree-like member of the Amelanchior group." The numerous Amelanchiors of many sizes and species found readily over most of temperate North America are probably more familiar under the name of Shadbush or Shadblow because along the Atlantic section of their range they flower about the time the shad run up the river to spawn. The white or occasionally pinkish flowers come just before the leaves and have 5 straplike petals, a mark of the clan. The fruit is berrylike, varying in size and color according to the species. The Serviceberry, illustrated here, may be anything from a shrub to a tree 60 feet tall and ranges from New Brunswick to Minnesota and southward to the Gulf States. The leaves are 2 to 4 inches long, the petals about ½ inch long, and the reddish-purple fruit about ⅜ inch in diameter and rather tasteless.

DOTTED HAW; DOTTED THORN
(*Crataegus punctata*)

The Haws of North America are a group of innumerable species of very thorny shrubs or small trees that grow
singly or in clumps and have crooked, twisted, and sometimes interwoven branches, Spring clusters of 5-petaled
white or pink flowers of the apple-blossom type, and Autumn fruit like tiny apples or rose hips, usually red, orange,
yellow, or some combination of such colors. The Dotted
Haw, shown here as a sample of the bewildering group, is
common in pastures and on dry, open hillsides from Maine
and Quebec to Minnesota and south to western Georgia
and Tennessee. It has slightly curved thorns 1 to 2 inches
long, leaves 2 to 3 inches long, and the fruit covered with
dots accounts for its name. But sorting out all the species
is an impossible task for a novice. In the words of King
Lear: "Oh! that way madness lies; let me shun that."

BIRD CHERRY; FIRE CHERRY; PIN CHERRY
(*Prunus pennsylvanica*)

Three widespread Wild Cherries of North America are this species and the two that
follow. To the beginner they may look somewhat alike, especially in the sapling stage, but
there is no difficulty in distinguishing one from the other if a little attention is paid to de-

tails of leaf, flower and fruit. For instance, this species
produces its ½-inch white flowers in "umbels" or
"corymbs," which means that the flowers and later the
¼-inch red cherries are on individual stalks or "pedicels" an inch or so in length, as shown. This immediately sets it apart from the Wild Black or Rum Cherry
and the Choke Cherry that flower in cylindrical
"racemes," an arrangement in which the individual
flowers and consequent fruit appear on short stalks
along and around a central axis. The illustration
shows why some persons call this the Pin Cherry. It is
called the Bird Cherry because of the fondness birds
have for its tart fruit and is known as the Fire Cherry
in some regions because it springs up quickly in burnt
areas. It is a northerly species, common across Canada and much of the northern section of the United
States. At best, it is a small tree with a short life span.
However, the tart fruit is tasty and the tree serves as
useful cover until better trees take over.

[54]

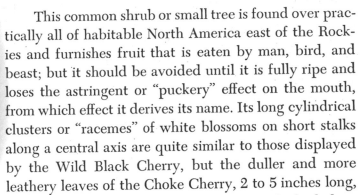

CHOKE CHERRY
(*Prunus virginiana*)

This common shrub or small tree is found over practically all of habitable North America east of the Rockies and furnishes fruit that is eaten by man, bird, and beast; but it should be avoided until it is fully ripe and loses the astringent or "puckery" effect on the mouth, from which effect it derives its name. Its long cylindrical clusters or "racemes" of white blossoms on short stalks along a central axis are quite similar to those displayed by the Wild Black Cherry, but the duller and more leathery leaves of the Choke Cherry, 2 to 5 inches long, have the wider part of the blade beyond the middle, which is not the case with the lighter and shinier leaves of the Wild Black Cherry. The easiest way to distinguish the Choke Cherry from the Wild Black Cherry is to glance at the ripe or ripening fruit. The 5-pointed flower calyx sticks to the developing fruit in the Wild Black Cherry, but there is no sign of it on the fruit of this species.

WILD BLACK CHERRY; RUM CHERRY
(*Prunus serotina*)

This is a valuable timber tree, as well as a source of tasty fruit, over the eastern half of temperate North America. In the sapling stage the bark is smooth and reddish-brown, but on the stout trunks of old trees it is dark gray and flaky. There are many species of Wild Cherry in North America but this and the Choke Cherry are the only ones that flower in cylindrical clusters. The illustration shows quite clearly the calyx that adheres to the fruit in this species and makes it an easy matter to distinguish it from the Choke Cherry. Once this difference is fixed in mind, the beginner will note differences in shape, texture, and general appearance of the leaves and will soon know the Wild Black Cherry from the Choke Cherry at a glance. The name Rum Cherry goes back to colonial days when the fruit of this species was used to flavor rum. It is said that the wilted leaves of the Wild Black Cherry are poisonous to cattle.

[55]

KENTUCKY COFFEE TREE

(Gymnocladus dioica)

Keep your eyes open for this tree because you never know where you will encounter one. Originally native in rich woodlands over a limited area of eastern and central North America, it has been planted to such an extent that now you may find it almost anywhere in the United States and southern Canada. It is common in public parks and on private estates and the offspring of such plantings often go over the fence and escape to the wild. The clusters of little flowers, wan white in color, are easily overlooked amid the foliage of late Spring, but the bark of the trunk and larger branches is distinctive, the leaves are truly remarkable, and the fruit pods are eye-catching curiosities that make most Kentucky Coffee Trees no trouble at all to identify with these odd objects clinging to the stark, gaunt, blunt branchlets through the leafless months of the year. Some of the trees bear only staminate or male flowers, and thus do not produce fruit, but more often the odd pods are hung out as a sign for all to see through Fall and Winter.

These pods are flat, leathery, and mahogany-colored, from 4 to 10 inches long and about 2 inches in width, and each one contains 2 or more blackish seeds about the size of lima beans. The Kentucky Coffee Tree is a relative of the lima bean, and of the string and butter beans and garden peas as well. All these and many other vegetables, flowers, and trees belong to the great Pulse, Pea, or Legume group, a large and famous family of the plant world that the botanists call the Leguminosae, the badge of which is the bean-type fruit.

Where the big pods of the Kentucky Coffee Tree are missing in the leafless season, it isn't difficult to recognize the tree by its blunt branchlets and the peculiar gray bark of a flaky appearance as though it had been daubed on with a palette knife by some painter of the French Impressionist school. The leaves that appear quite late in Spring are doubly compound and really astonishing in size. They may be 3 feet long and 2 feet wide and have 100 or more 1½-inch leaflets, as shown in the illustration.

HONEY LOCUST; HONEY-SHUCK

(Gleditsia triacanthos)

As the long seed pods show, this is another member of the Legume group. It is also the thorniest large tree in North America. The Haws, to be sure, are thickly armed with stiletto-like thorns pointing in all directions, but the Haws are shrubs or small trees, whereas the Honey Locust that is now found over most of the eastern half of the United States and adjacent Canada is a stalwart tree at maturity and sometimes is well over 100 feet in height. On many of the larger Honey Locusts the dark gray bark, sandpapery in texture, is covered with fearsome compound thorns almost down to the ground, but on other trees the lower trunk is clear and the "barbed wire entanglements" begin with the main branches and continue all the way out to the many, crooked, thin, drooping branchlets that are a feature of the tree. There is one variety that has no thorns at all, but it is an oddity and rarely encountered except in cultivation.

The compound thorns are only one notable feature of the Honey Locust, or Honey-shuck as it is known in some regions. The leaves are quite distinctive, too. They may be doubly compound, like those of the Kentucky Coffee Tree though in a much smaller way,

but most of them are merely compound and they usually sprout in clusters along the branchlets. They average 8 or 9 inches in length and have 7 to 10 pairs of narrowly oval leaflets about an inch long. But the most striking feature of this tree and the one that accounts for its name of Honey Locust is the long, twisting fruit pod that contains not only numerous flat oval seeds but a sweet pulpy substance with a flavor not unlike that of honey. When ripe in early Autumn, these twisted, ribbon-like and fairly stiff pods are a darkish red-brown in color, 8 to 18 inches long, and about 1 inch wide. Some of them cling to the bare branches long after the leaves have vanished but many fall with the leaves to litter the ground and become tasty food for cattle, rabbits, squirrels, birds, and other creatures of the wild. Those neighborhood children who know a good thing when they see one will open the pod, discard the seeds and chew on the pod for the sake of the sweet substance that coats its inner surface. Try it yourself. It's good.

REDBUD; JUDAS TREE

(Cercis canadensis)

Because of its attractive flowers, many persons know the Redbud as a cultivated shrub or small tree over most of temperate North America, but in the wild it is found in the undergrowth of rich woods from New Jersey to Nebraska and southward to the Gulf Coast. It really has red buds in Winter; and in the Spring, before the leaves appear, it produces abundant clusters of rose-purple flowers that seem to grow right out of the dark bark

of the branches. That's the time of year when it is easiest to track down the Redbud in the wild, but it may be recognized later by the roundish heart-shaped leaves that measure 3 to 5 inches in any direction or by the 3-inch beans that are its seed pods and that cling to the branches through the Autumn. The flowers of the pea type and the beans show that it is a member of the great family of "Legumes." The name Judas Tree comes from the legend that it was on a Near Eastern tree of this type that Judas hanged himself and that its flowers, white at the time, turned color with shame and have blushed ever since. Look for the flowers as the birds come north in Spring.

YELLOWWOOD; VIRGILIA

(Cladrastis lutea)

This is an exceptional tree in several respects. It is rare in the wild over its narrow, native inland range and common in cultivation over the greater part of the United States. It is a tree of medium size that is highly prized for the lavish supply of drooping clusters of cream-white, pea-type flowers in late Spring. The fruit pod is a light, thin bean 3 to 4 inches long and, as it often clings to the bare branches through the Winter, it is an aid in recognizing the tree. The bark is smooth and gray like that of the Beech and underneath it the wood is a bright yellow that even a shallow incision will show. The compound leaves are about 1 foot long; the 2-inch oval leaflets are not usually opposite one another along the axis. And next year's buds are under the petioles!

[58]

COMMON LOCUST; BLACK LOCUST

(Robinia pseudo-acacia)

If a farmer calls a tree a Locust without any further description, this is the species he means. From its original narrow range along the Appalachians, it has spread by cultivation and escape over the eastern half of the continent. It grows to be a tall, narrow tree of picturesque appeal, with twistingly corrugated brownish-gray bark, graceful and delicate compound leaves and, in Spring or early Summer, drooping clusters of sweet-smelling, cream-white, pea-type flowers that, along with the 3-inch beans they ultimately produce, prove its membership in the Pulse or Legume family. The leaves may be a foot or more in length with 7 to 21 oval leaflets 1 to 1½ inches long. The tree grows quickly, provides valuable timber, and has other good qualities, but it also has faults. It carries stout and sharp little thorns on its branches, spreads rapidly where it isn't wanted and is desperately stubborn in resisting eviction from such places.

WAFER-ASH; HOP TREE

(Ptelea trifolia)

This is a common enough shrub or small tree from Quebec to Nebraska and south to the Gulf States, but it generally escapes notice unless the dry seed clusters catch the eye where they cling late in the year after the leaves have fallen. These "wafers"—circular samaras to the botanist—are about ¾ inch in diameter and the product of a spray or "compound

cyme" of greenish-white little flowers that appear in June or July. The compound leaves are long-stalked or "petioled," as shown, and the 3 leaflets, pointed at both ends, may be 2 to 6 inches long. The crushed leaves smell something like the hops used in brewing, which explains the name Hop Tree sometimes applied to it. The branches of the Wafer-Ash are favorite places of deposit for the linear whitish egg masses of one of the odd-looking "Brownie Bugs," the triangular *Echinops binotata*. The parent insects often are found on the Wafer-Ash and, if you carry a pocket magnifying glass, it is worth while taking a look at them.

AILANTHUS
(*Ailanthus altissima*)

The name Ailanthus is alleged to mean "Tree of Heaven" in some Moluccan dialect and is a reference to the height of 100 feet it sometimes reaches in Asia, to which it is native; but in North America, where it is now widespread, it doesn't grow to any such commanding height nor has it gained any such high-flown title. In fact, because of the offensive odor of the staminate flowers, the crushed leaves, or the bruised bark, it is often inelegantly called "Stinkweed." It is a hardy tree, growing on almost any kind of ground and springing up quickly in vacant city lots. The clusters (panicles) of greenish-yellow staminate and pistillate flowers are produced on separate trees. The pistillate clusters have no offensive odor and produce masses of colorful seed-carrying "samaras" 1 to 2 inches in length, which are yellow with a crimson blush. The compound leaves may be 2 to 4 feet in length with 11 to 31 leaflets, 2 to 5 inches long, and shaped as shown.

STAGHORN SUMAC
(*Rhus typhina*)

This is the most widespread of the three harmless and handsome Sumacs—the Staghorn, the Smooth, and the Dwarf or Wing-rib Sumac—that are found in abundance over most of eastern North America. They are much similar in general appearance and fruiting habit and their compound leaves turn a brilliant crimson that adds color to the Autumn

fields. It's the soft brown hairy growth on the younger branches that gives the name Staghorn to this species. The inconspicuous little flowers come in pyramidal clusters and the pistillate clusters turn into attractive cone-shaped masses of tiny seeds enclosed in hairy coverings. The compound leaves may be 2 feet or more in length with numerous leaflets, shaped as shown. They differ decidedly from the Ailanthus leaflets in that they are sharply toothed in a small way, and furthermore a drop of milky sap will appear if you pluck a Sumac leaflet. The Smooth Sumac will be known by its smooth branchlets and the Dwarf Sumac by the "wings" along the leaf axis between leaflets.

POISON SUMAC
(*Rhus vernix*)

To offset three friendly, handsome, and harmless Sumacs, there are three nasty members of the group. They are the Poison Sumac, the Poison Ivy, and the much similar but more southerly Poison Oak. The only good thing about Poison Sumac is its comparative scarcity over a range that covers the eastern half of the United States and adjacent Canada. It's a shrub or small tree up to 25 feet in height and is found almost exclusively in swamps or wet ground. The compound leaves are 1 to 2 feet long and the 7 to 13 leaflets, 2 to 3 inches long, are red-veined, shiny above and smooth along the edge. The flower and fruit clusters are more open than those of the harmless Sumacs and the sprays of off-white or soapy-looking little berries or "drupes" usually hang on through the Winter and help to identify the species. However, some plants do not fruit, so try to learn the whereabouts of the Poison Sumac when it is in leaf—and then keep away from it. As a skin irritant it is worse than Poison Ivy.

POISON IVY
(*Rhus radicans*)

It might be a good idea to have the first lesson in botany consist of teaching a child to recognize Poison Ivy because it is found almost everywhere in temperate North Amer-

ica and ignorance of its appearance has caused much suffering to countless victims. It is a shrub or climbing vine that is easily recognized when in foliage by its long-stalked compound leaves made up of 3 shiny leaflets, shaped as shown. The leaflets, 1 to 4 inches long, may be smooth-edged or bluntly toothed. It's a good thing to note all the details and become thoroughly familiar with the variations in the leaflets so that the plant may be recognized the more easily. It flowers and fruits much like the Poison Sumac but the clusters are more compact and the Poison Ivy berries or "drupes" are not shiny but a dull gray. Where you see such clusters of dried fruits in Fall or Winter on a shrub or along a climbing vine, keep away!

AMERICAN HOLLY
(*Ilex opaca*)

The Holly wreath, made of this or the much similar European Holly, conveys the Christmas spirit far and wide in happy homes. The American Holly is found as a thick shrub or a tree up to 50 feet or more in height with a tight-fitting, dappled gray bark, evergreen foliage consisting of thick, leathery, spiny-tipped leaves 2 to 3 inches long and, in season, the attractive red berries or "drupes" about ¼ inch in diameter that contrast so brilliantly with the dark green foliage. Though it grows as far north in the wild as the coastal region of Massachusetts, it is more at home in the South and reaches its greatest size well below the Mason-Dixon line. It flourishes in moist woodlands from the Gulf States to Illinois and Indiana, and is common through the Atlantic States northward to New Jersey. It has numerous close relatives in North America, including some with red berries and others with yellow or black fruit, but none with the combination of red fruit and spiny-tipped evergreen leaves that distinguish this species.

BLACK ALDER; WINTERBERRY
(*Ilex verticillata*)

Of a gray day in November or December, the beautiful little black-tipped red berries or "drupes" along the dark branchlets of the Black Alder lend a welcome touch of color to a stark and leafless landscape. Seldom growing to tree size, it usually is found as a shrub 6 to 12 feet high in swamps, wet meadows, and along the shores of ponds and lakes from Newfoundland to Minnesota and south to Georgia and Missouri. It is a true Holly or *Ilex.* The common name of Black Alder comes from the fact that it often grows among Alders and its leaves, shaped as shown and about 2 inches long on the average, turn blackish in Autumn. The greenish flowers come after the shrub is in full leaf and few persons notice the inconspicuous little staminate and pistillate clusters that appear in the angles or "axils" where the leaf stalks emerge from the branchlets. In fact, few persons recognize or pay any attention to the Black Alder or Winterberry until the bright red berries, about ⅓ inch in diameter, catch the eye in Autumn.

BLADDERNUT

(*Staphylea trifolia*)

This shrub or small tree probably would be completely overlooked were it not for the persistent seed pods that cling to the leafless branches through Autumn and early Winter and challenge attention in the form of inflated capsules about 2 inches long, usually divided into 3 sections with a seed in each section. It is found in rich woods and thickets and occasionally along forest borders or roadsides from Quebec to Minnesota and south to Georgia and Oklahoma. It is often seen in cultivation for the sake of the curious "bladders" that earn it the common name of Bladdernut. The compound leaves grow opposite one another and usually consist of 3 oval leaflets 2 to 3 inches long. The 3 leaflets account for the *trifolia* of its scientific name. The *Staphylea* comes from the Greek for "a bunch of grapes" and refers to the somewhat grape-like drooping clusters of small 5-petaled white flowers in Spring and the consequent pendent pods that catch the eye later.

NORWAY MAPLE

(*Acer platanoides*)

We have many native Maples in North America but this species, introduced from Europe because of its handsome appearance, regular habit of growth, and disease-resistant qualities, is now a common sight to "city folk" over most of the United States. It has been planted extensively along city streets, highways, parkways, driveways, and byways in all directions. Its wonderful sprays of flowers in Spring would be admired by millions except for the fact that they are light green in color and most persons mistake them for early foliage. The large 5-lobed leaves may be 7 inches wide and the "keys" or "samaras" that show it to be of the Maple family are set at the widest angle of all Maple keys. The bark of the trunk is regularly ribbed somewhat like that of the White Ash. A clinching detail for recognition is the drop of milky juice that appears at the base of the leaf stalk or "petiole" when plucked from the branchlet. But the bark, flower sprays, and keys should be enough.

[63]

SUGAR MAPLE
(*Acer saccharum*)

The great Maples of North America, a noble family with many tall, handsome, and useful representatives, flourish in field and forest from the Atlantic to the Pacific and from Mexico to the Arctic Circle. They are among the finest of our "hardwoods" and produce good lumber, including the "curly maple" and "bird's-eye maple" cherished by woodworkers. A family trait is that the leaves grow opposite one another on the branchlets but the real badge of the clan is the fruit, the Maple "key" that is really 2 winged seeds joined together in growth.

The stalwart Sugar Maples that sometimes reach a height of 100 feet or more are found from the Gaspé Peninsula to Manitoba and south to the Gulf States, but they are at their best and most abundant in the mixed forests of the Great Lakes States, New England, and southern Canada. Incidentally, this is the tree that gave Canada its emblem, the Maple Leaf. It is also the tree that in the northern part of its range, produces the sap that, through spile and bucket and boiling down amid the wild winds and late snows of March and April, becomes the maple syrup and maple sugar of commerce. Where "sap boiling" is a regular Spring custom, a grove of these Maples— usually referred to as a "sugar bush"—is a valued possession.

For the most part it is not particularly difficult, even for a beginner, to distinguish one species of Maple from another, but it so happens that there is a Black Maple (*Acer nigrum*) found over much of the range of the Sugar Maple and the resemblance is such that some botanists still insist that it is merely a variety of the Sugar Maple. In any event, they have the same sweet sap and similar keys but the leaf of the Sugar Maple, 3 to 8 inches broad, usually is 5-lobed, as shown, and firmly flat in contrast to the usually 3-lobed Black Maple leaf that tends to be droopy at the edges. The name Black Maple refers to the bark, which is darker than that of the Sugar Maple and not as coarsely ridged or plated. Also, the Black Maple prefers rich bottomland while the Sugar Maple is a climber and likes slopes and well-drained uplands. The greenish-yellow flowers of the Sugar Maple are not presented in flamboyant clusters like those of the Norway Maple but hang modestly and almost shyly on thin stalks or pedicels 2 to 4 inches long amid the early foliage.

[64]

RED MAPLE

(Acer rubrum)

This is a Maple of medium size found mostly in swamps and wet ground over the eastern half of the United States and adjacent Canada. Twice a year the Red Maple puts on an advertising campaign to attract public notice and advertise its name. In early Spring, long before its leaves appear, it hangs out untold numbers of beautiful little red flowers that, before very long, turn into "keys" that are strongly tinted with red. Furthermore, the young leaves appear on red stalks or "petioles," though this often escapes notice, just as do the red twigs and the red buds it displays through the Winter. But again in Autumn it calls attention to itself in a spectacular way. It is so often found in swamps that many farmers call it the Swamp Maple and one of the first signs of Autumn is the turning of the leaves of the Red Maples in the swamps. They turn red, of course; a bright red that is in striking contrast with the sober green foliage still worn by most of its neighbors.

It's rather helpful to the beginner when a tree lives up to its common name as the Red Maple does in eastern North America and as the Big-leaf Maple does along the Pacific Coast with its enormous leaves up to 12 inches or more in width. The leaves of the Red Maple are quite modest in size, averaging about 4 inches in width. They are usually 3-lobed and appear to be so even when they are 5-lobed because the 2 lower lobes, when present, are more like mere bumps than distinct lobes. They are smaller than the 3-lobed leaves of the Black Maple and much more toothed along the outlines of the lobes. The bark also helps to distinguish the Red Maple. On older trees the lower bark of the trunk is dark gray and somewhat pebbly or wrinkled and ridged, but higher up and on the branches it is a smooth and light gray that, sighted through gaps in green foliage, often looks almost white.

By the way, keep your eyes open for the Sycamore Maple (*Acer pseudoplatanus*), an introduced species widely planted as a shade tree not only in the East but along the Pacific Coast. It has large, thick, 5-lobed leaves and its flowers and keys hang down like bunches of grapes.

[65]

SILVER MAPLE
(*Acer saccharinum*)

It's the silvery lower surface of the foliage, which shows in striking contrast to the sober green of the upper surface when the wind tosses the branches about, that gives this tree its name. It's a weak sister among the Maples. Though it often grows to be a fairly large tree, it is never a strong one and often loses limbs in storms. It is common, mostly in moist ground, from New Brunswick to Minnesota and south to the Gulf States. You will know it by the slashed appearance of its much-toothed, deeply-cut, 5-lobed leaves about 5 inches in diameter, its long drooping branchlets that curve up sharply toward the tips, the widespread keys, and the flaky gray bark of the trunk. There are other Maples, native and imported, that are not shown in this book but all may be recognized as Maples by their opposite leaves and the "keys" that are the badge of the clan.

BOX ELDER; ASH-LEAVED MAPLE
(*Acer negundo*)

This is a Maple that, in most places, lives under an assumed name. It's a small and friendly tree that likes to be near water, but it is much cultivated and may be found in good ground almost anywhere in temperate North America east of the Rockies. Over this wide range it is commonly called the Box Elder and certainly its compound leaves would never lead the ordinary person to link it with the familiar Maples of the countryside, but the typical Maple "keys" that are its fruit settle the issue. These keys, produced only on the trees that bear pistillate flowers, hang in thick clusters, as shown. The compound leaves, which have the family trait of growing opposite one another on the branchlets, may have 3, 5, 7, or 9 leaflets and the leaflets may be sparsely toothed or even lobed. The bark of the trunk and branches is brown and only slightly ridged. The foliage, though variable, is quite distinctive.

HORSE CHESTNUT

(*Aesculus hippocastanum*)

Under a spreading chestnut-tree
The village smithy stands;
The smith, a mighty man is he,
With large and sinewy hands;
And the muscles of his brawny arms
Are strong as iron bands.

So wrote Longfellow a century ago when the village blacksmith shop was a center of activity and a clearing house for local news. The inspiration for the verse was a blacksmith shop that the poet passed in going to and from his Cambridge home when he was teaching at Harvard. The popularity of the poem brought many persons to see the "village smithy" and some visitors were surprised to find that the "spreading chestnut" of poetic fame was not our native and noble Chestnut but the Horse Chestnut pictured here. This tree of southwestern Asia and ancient days in Greece followed the march of civilization across Europe, where it now may be seen along the streets and in the parks of many great cities, and was brought to North America about 200 years ago to flourish in much the same way here.

It belongs to a group, including our native Buckeyes, that has much similar flower clusters, "palmately" compound leaves growing opposite one another on the branchlets, and the curiously marked fruit called "horse chestnuts" or "buckeyes" typical of the group. However, there are differences that are easily noted. If in doubt, the color of the flowers, the number, shape, and size of the leaflets in the compound leaves, the shape, size, and prickliness or lack of it in the coverings of the fruit pods, and the gumminess or lack of it on Winter buds will enable you to track down the species. For instance, the Horse Chestnut usually has 7 radiating leaflets in its compound leaves whereas the Buckeyes usually have 5, and the Horse Chestnut leaves average larger, with the central leaflet sometimes 10 inches or more in length. The upright clusters of white flowers flecked with red, the very prickly pods, and the very gummy Winter buds are other features of the Horse Chestnut.

OHIO BUCKEYE
(Aesculus glabra)

This illustrates what was stated of the Buckeye group on the previous page. You may encounter one or more of our five or six native species of Buckeye almost anywhere from New York to California and southward to the Gulf States and they vary in size from shrubs to tall trees. The Ohio Buckeye, also called the Fetid Buckeye because the bruised bark or crushed foliage gives off a bad odor, is usually a small tree with long-stalked leaves, greenish-yellow flower clusters, and fruit husks that are mildly prickled or roughly pebbled. The "buckeyes" are about 1 inch in diameter and the leaflets of the compound leaves 3 to 6 inches long. The illustration shows 5 leaflets, which is the common rule among Buckeyes, but sometimes you will find 6 or 7 leaflets. You will also find other species of Buckeye with red, yellow, or even purple flowers, leaflets of different size, and fruit husks of different texture and shape.

WESTERN SOAPBERRY
(Sapindus drummondii)

This is a native tree of the Southwest that often is confused with the naturalized Chinaberry or Pride-of-India Tree (*Melia azedarach*) found in dooryards or along village streets in the warmer portions of the United States, particularly the Southeast. The confusion is caused by the much similar clusters of dried yellowish berries or "drupes," about ½ inch or more in diameter, that cling to the trees through the Winter. However, there are differences easily noted. The flower clusters of the Soapberry are white or greenish-white, whereas the slightly larger flower clusters of the Chinaberry usually are purple or pale lilac. The compound leaves of the Soapberry, about 1 foot long, have 9 to 19 leaflets, shaped as shown, and smooth along the edges. The larger leaves of the Chinaberry are doubly compound and the leaflets are toothed or lobed. The berries of the Soapberry will produce a lather if crushed in water.

[68]

BASSWOOD; LINDEN

(*Tilia americana*)

The American Basswoods are the counterparts of the European Lindens and either name will serve well enough to identify the trees, though Basswood seems to be the preference of farmers and woodsmen who find them in the wild on this side of the Atlantic. There are three or four species native to the eastern half of temperate North America and several European species have been much planted along city streets, in public parks, and on suburban lawns for shade or decorative purposes. To the ordinary eye all these different species are much similar in general appearance and the beginner will do well to forget about specific differences for a time and be content to learn to recognize one and all Basswoods or Lindens as such at first sight. This is a very easy matter over a considerable portion of the year because of the odd way in which the clusters of flowers and subsequent fruit hang from the approximate centers of what look like very narrow leaves but are "bracts" to the botanist. The illustration shows this plainly and the fact that the clusters of dried, pea-like nutlets often hang on the trees after the leaves have fallen is a further aid in identification.

The species shown here is by far the most widespread and abundant of our native Basswoods and in late Spring or early Summer it is laden with delightfully fragrant clus-

ters of little cream-colored flowers that are nectar and ambrosia to Honeybees. At such times you can actually locate the tree "by ear" because of the hum made by the myriad bees in their activity around the flower clusters. The beekeepers in some regions pay tribute to these trees by referring to the early season, light-colored product of the hive as Basswood honey as distinguished from the later and darker product they call Buckwheat honey. But a closer bond between the bees and the trees is that the light wooden frames in which honey is sold in the comb are made of Basswood. The heart-shaped, sharptoothed leaf blades of this species may be as much as 8 inches long but average about 5 inches in length. The dark bark of the trunk and branches, reddish twigs, and dark red buds help to identify the Basswood or Linden in Winter. It is a fine shade tree and is much planted along city streets.

[69]

SOUR GUM; TUPELO; PEPPERIDGE

(Nyssa sylvatica)

This in an interesting and attractive tree even though it never grows beyond medium height. It is variously known as Sour Gum, Black Gum, Tupelo, Pepperidge, Hornpipe, Beetle-bung, and Snag Tree and possibly has a few other local titles over a range that extends from Maine to Michigan and south to the Gulf States. It prefers wet ground and often is found in or along the borders of swamps, but it can and does thrive on slopes and good upland territory. The leaves, shaped as shown, are 2 to 5 inches long and such a lustrous green on the upper surface in Summer that they fairly glisten where the sunlight strikes them. In the Autumn they turn a deep rich red so distinctive that the tree can be recognized at a distance by that feature alone.

For the beginner, of course, the easiest way to recognize the Sour Gum is by the fruit that usually is produced in abundance, though some trees bear only staminate or male flowers and produce no fruit. You will note in the illustration that the oval, berry-like "drupes," about ⅓ inch long and blue-black when ripe, appear on long stalks and may be single or as many as 4 to a cluster. They really do not have much "meat" on them because the stone inside takes up so much room. Furthermore, they have a slightly acid taste. But apparently this makes no difference to the Robins, Mourning Doves and other birds that flock to the feasting when this fruit ripens in the early Fall.

In the leafless season you may recognize the Sour Gum by the deeply corrugated dark gray bark of the trunk that, on mature trees, contrasts sharply with the smooth light gray bark of the many short branches that stick straight out horizontally or, in many cases, slant downward. The famous Cotton Gum (*Nyssa aquatica*) of the southern swamps, a close relative, is a bigger tree with a buttressed trunk, odd-shaped leaves and fruit an inch long.

FLOWERING DOGWOOD

(Cornus florida)

Everybody can recognize the Flowering Dogwood when it's in bright bloom in the Spring, but there are some things about this popular small tree that often are overlooked or perhaps not known by the average observer. The flowers, for instance, are not what they seem. The 4 broad, notched, cream-white or occasionally pink divisions that catch the eye and that most persons take to be petals are something quite different. If you wish to see them in an earlier stage, look at the picture of the bare branchlets as you find them in the colder months when the leaves are off. Each tiny, pear-shaped, sharp-tipped object is a future flower group enclosed by a wrapping of 4 "bracts" as the botanists call them. The wrappings hold tight until "Spring unlocks the flowers to paint the laughing soil" as Reginald Heber put it. Then the wrappings unfold, expand, and change color to form a handsome frame for the true flowers, the little greenish-yellow objects in the small circle in the center.

If you look at the true flowers, you will find that they have 4 petals and it's well to keep this in mind because there are many species of native Dogwood in North America and only a few have the colorful bracts that make this species notable over the eastern half of the United States and adjacent Canada. The more northerly midget member of the clan, the Dwarf Cornel or Bunchberry (*Cornus canadensis*) has similar bracts and the Pacific Dogwood (*Cornus nuttalli*) which grows to be a tree of good size, usually has 6 such colorful bracts, but where these are missing, the 4 petals of the little Dogwood flowers distinguish them immediately from the 5-lobed Viburnum flowers that grow in similar clusters and often are found side by side with the Dogwoods. The fruits of the Dogwoods are berry-like "drupes" that are fine food for many birds. Those of the Flowering Dogwood are, as shown, bright red in color, black-tipped, and somewhat oval in shape. The colorful bracts in the Spring, the bright berries of early Autumn, and the tiny, pear-shaped Winter packages of future flower clusters mark the Flowering Dogwood.

RED-OSIER DOGWOOD

(*Cornus stolonifera*)

This is one of the many native species of Dog-wood that usually go unrecognized because at first glance they look nothing like the well-known Flowering Dogwood. In fact, they look more like Viburnums and, since they often are found in company with Viburnums and produce similar flattish clusters of little cream-white flowers, there is some excuse for confusion. But when in bloom, the flowers tell the tale. The tiny Dogwood flowers have 4 petals. The little faces of the Viburnum flowers are distinctly 5-lobed. Later you may note how the veins of the Dogwood leaf curve sharply toward the tip along the edge of the leaf. The name of this species comes from the deep red or wine-purple color of the stems and branches, a feature particularly noticeable in northern Winters. The Silky Cornel or Kinnikinnik (*Cornus amomum*), another of the clan, has much similar colorful branches but in that species the pith is brown; in the Red-osier it is white. Such are the details that help the beginner to sort out the Dog-woods.

PERSIMMON

(*Diospyros virginiana*)

From Pennsylvania to Iowa and south to the Gulf States the Persimmon is well and favorably known for the smooth, round, orange-colored, edible fruit that it produces. It takes a touch of cold weather to ripen the fruit and anyone who "jumps the season" does so at the risk of setting his or her teeth on edge. The leaves of the Persimmon, shaped as shown, and quite shiny on the upper surface, are 3 to 7 inches long. The tree is ordinarily of medium size but in the Mississippi Basin some Persimmons have reached 100 feet in height. The bark of the older trees is ruggedly corrugated and looks even more like alligator hide than the bark of the Sassafras. A feature of the Persimmon is that the fruit clings to the tree long after the leaves have fallen and the dried calyx of the flower likewise clings to the fruit until it meets its fate, consumption or dissolution. The Persimmon may be found in New York and New England but it is primarily a southern tree.

WHITE ASH

(Fraxinus americana)

There are Red, White, and Blue Ashes but this combination of colorful names has no patriotic or narrowly geographical significance. It's true that the Red, White, and Blue Ashes are native residents of the United States but they live and thrive in Canada, too. Few regions of temperate North America are without some representative Ash and many areas can boast half a dozen or more species and varieties. The hardy Black Ash pushes northward almost to the shores of Hudson Bay. The Water Ash sticks to the southeastern portion of the United States. The Oregon Ash prefers the Pacific Coast for residential purposes.

For the beginner, sifting the Ashes (no offense!) will be quite a task and will take some time and study. A good start can be made by becoming acquainted with the White Ash, one of the outstanding members of a fine tribe, a tall and shapely tree of clean limbs and lovely foliage. It's a good shade tree for lawns and also one of the most valuable timber trees in the forests of North America. When you know the White Ash, you will have no trouble in recognizing other Ashes as Ashes, but there may be some difficulty in tracking down the species or variety.

There are three things by which the Ashes may be known. The first is that they have compound leaves. The second is that these compound leaves grow opposite one another along the branchlets. The third item is the typical winged seed that usually is produced in abundant clusters except on those trees that bear only male or staminate flowers and, happily, they are in the minority. The White Ash, which is found from Quebec to Minnesota and southward to Georgia and Texas, has a trunk with grayish-brown bark with a neat network of narrow ridged hollows running up and down. The compound leaves, 8 to 15 inches long, have 5 to 9 leaflets, shaped as shown, and 2 to 6 inches long. Note that the leaflets have stalks about ½ inch long. The "samara" or winged seed is 1 to 2 inches long. The various species of Ash are distinguished by differences in detail of bark and bud, leaf and branch, flower and seed, but all Ashes have opposite compound leaves and the typical winged seeds of the tribe that, by the way, are much liked by many birds.

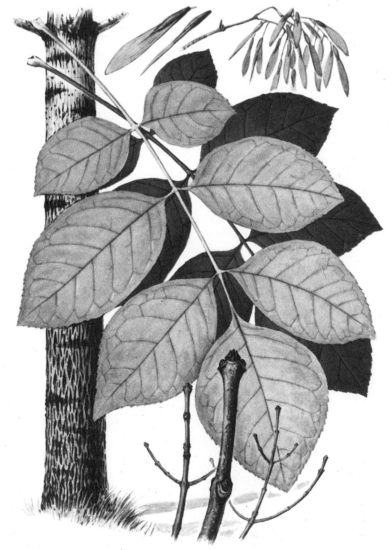

COMMON CATALPA; INDIAN BEAN

(Catalpa bignonioides)

The Catalpas are medium-sized trees with huge broad leaves, pyramidal clusters or "panicles" of 2-lipped, bell-shaped, showy white flowers, and seed pods that look like long, thin beans but are capsules that eventually split open and release innumerable winged seeds. The dried capsules or their twisted remnants usually cling to the tree through most of the Winter. The leaves are 6 to 12 inches long and the seed capsules sometimes reach 20 inches in length. In this species the throat of each flower is streaked with yellow and much dotted with purple. In the very similar Western Catalpa *(Catalpa speciosa)*, the leaves are a bit larger and much more pointed at the tip, the seed capsules are thicker, and the fewer flowers in the more open clusters have little or no purple spotting in the throat. The introduced Paulownia has somewhat similar large leaves and pyramidal flower clusters but the flowers are pale blue. In the leafless season the Paulownia may be known by its oval, empty seed pods and coming flower sprays in velvet bud.

BUTTONBUSH
(Cephalanthus occidentalis)

This is a common to abundant shrub in swamps and wet ground generally and grows to tree size only in the southern part of its broad range that extends from the Atlantic to the Pacific in temperate North America. It has crooked or curving branches and the shiny and narrowly oval leaves, 4 to 7 inches long, are late in appearing in Spring. However, there is no need to go into details of bark, bud, or leaf because the flower and seed clusters are easy marks by which the shrub may be known. The round clusters of little cream-colored flowers are about 1 inch in diameter and they appear on long stalks or "peduncles" in late Spring or Summer. They quickly condense to spherical seed clusters, about ¾ inch in diameter, that turn brown as the seed ripen and hang on through most of the Winter. You can't miss them.

NANNYBERRY

(Viburnum lentago)

Every section of temperate North America has on display one or more of our many native species of Viburnum, all of which have such traits in common as simple leaves that grow opposite one another along the branchlets, flattish clusters or "compound cymes" of little 5-lobed mostly white or cream-colored flowers, and fruit in the form of small, 1-seeded berries or "drupes." Most of our Viburnums are shrubs but a few reach tree size, including the Nannyberry that ranges from Quebec to Manitoba and south to Georgia and Colorado and may be anything from a large shrub to a tree 30 feet or more in height. The flowering clusters are 2 to 5 inches in diameter and the berries, about ½ inch long, are blue-black when ripe. The leaves, shaped as shown, are minutely sharp-toothed and 2½ to 5 inches long. A much similar species, the Black or Sweet Haw (*Viburnum prunifolium*) has smaller leaves and flower clusters and is more southerly in range, reaching down to the Gulf Coast.

SOUTHERN ARROWWOOD

(Viburnum dentatum)

This and another species of Arrowwood (*Viburnum recognitum*), more northerly in range, are shrubs up to 10 feet or so in height that are commonly found in moist ground and along the borders of swamps, ponds, and streams from New Brunswick to Ontario and Michigan and south to South Carolina and Tennessee. The distinction between the two species is based on the amount of hairiness on the twigs, the "petioles," and the leaves, and a difference in the type of groove in the seed or stone of the fruit, but the beginner can let that go until later and lump the Arrowwoods together for the time being. The clusters of little white or cream-colored 5-lobed flowers are from 1 to 4 inches in diameter and the ripe berries or "drupes," about ¼ inch long, are blue-black. The leaves, shaped and toothed as shown in the illustration, have stalks or petioles about 1 inch long and leaf blades 1 to 4 inches long. If you go walking in wet ground, you are sure to run into Arrowwood.

MAPLE-LEAVED VIBURNUM
(Viburnum acerifolium)

This is a shrub up to 6 feet in height that is found in the undergrowth of dry or rocky woods from Quebec to Minnesota and south to Georgia and Tennessee. It is called Dockmackie in some regions but Maple-leaved Viburnum is the perfect name for it. From the shape, size, and texture of the leaves, it might be mistaken for an infant Maple but the flowers and fruit prove it to be one of the Viburnums. The leaves are 2 to 4 inches broad and the flat sprays or "cymes" of little cream-colored or sometimes pinkish 5-lobed flowers are 1 to 4 inches in diameter. The small, ovoid, 1-seeded berries or "drupes" that come later are purplish-black when ripe. The Arrowwoods, the Nanny-berry and the Maple-leaved Viburnum are just a few of the many Viburnums native to North America but an acquaintance with them will give the beginner a knowledge of the flowering and fruiting processes of the group and other species will soon be recognized.

RED-BERRIED ELDER
(Sambucus pubens)

Everybody knows the common "Elderberry" (Sambucus canadensis), the familiar roadside shrub with the compound leaves, the flat sprays of cream-colored flowers much like those of the Viburnums, and the later abundance of dark, juicy fruit often served up in tarts or pies or turned into "Elderberry wine." This is a taller, wilder, and red-fruited relative that may be found blooming much earlier in cool woods over most of temperate North America. The flower and fruit clusters in this species are not flat but rather pyramidal in shape. Other differences are that the Common Elder leaves have 5 to 11 leaflets whereas the Red-berried Elder more often displays only 5 to 7 typical Elder leaflets, shaped and toothed as shown. When leaf and fruit have gone, the brown pith of the stem or branch will distinguish this species from the Common Elder, which has white pith.

[76]

EUCALYPTUS; BLUE GUM

(*Eucalyptus globulus*)

Where you find any Eucalyptus in North America, you have reached cultivated ground because these are imported trees. There are scores of species of Eucalyptus in that vast region of the Southern Hemisphere known as Australasia. Just about a century ago, more than a dozen species were introduced into California and of that group the Blue Gum has been most successful in making itself at home on North American soil. It is a common sight almost anywhere at low altitude in California and has been much planted in Arizona and New Mexico as well as all along the Gulf Coast from Texas to Florida. A fast grower, at maturity it is a very tall and rather slim evergreen with willow-like leaves 6 to 12 inches long and brown outer bark that peels off in long straggling strips to expose the gray inner bark in a way to suggest the dappled or piebald bark of the Sycamores. The funnel-shaped whitish flowers, about 1½ inches broad, appear in the leaf axils along the branchlets and ultimately produce the curious seed capsules, shaped as shown, and up to about 1 inch across the top. Bark and bud as well as leaf, flower, and fruit contain an aromatic oil that is often used for medicinal purposes.

❋   ❋   ❋   ❋   ❋

Reader, this is as far as we can go together. But let neither of us stop learning because we have come to the end of a book. We never can come to an end of the wonders and beauties of Nature. The more we know of such matters, the greater enjoyment we find in living. As we close this book let the last words be from Milton:

To-morrow to fresh woods, and pastures new.

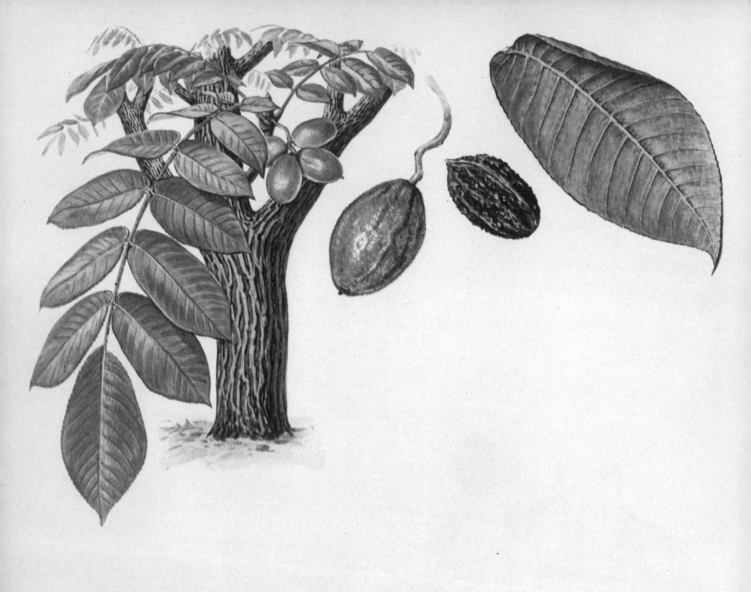